LET'S TREK

The Budget Traveller's Guide to
Federation Worlds

James Van Hise

PIONEER BOOKS INC

Recently Released Pioneer Books...

MTV: MUSIC YOU CAN SEE	ISBN#1-55698-355-7
TREK: THE NEXT GENERATION CREW BOOK	ISBN#1-55698-363-8
TREK: THE PRINTED ADVENTURES	ISBN#1-55698-365-5
THE CLASSIC TREK CREW BOOK	ISBN#1-55698-368-9
TREK VS THE NEXT GENERATION	ISBN#1-55698-370-0
TREK: THE NEXT GENERATION TRIBUTE BOOK	ISBN#1-55698-366-2
THE HOLLYWOOD CELEBRITY DEATH BOOK	ISBN#1-55698-369-7
LET'S TALK: AMERICA'S FAVORITE TV TALK SHOW HOSTS	ISBN#1-55698-364-6
HOT-BLOODED DINOSAUR MOVIES	ISBN#1-55698~365-4
BONANZA: THE UNOFFICIAL STORY OF THE PONDEROSA	ISBN#1-55698-359-X
THE KUNG FU BOOK	ISBN#1-55698-328-X
TREK: THE DEEP SPACE CELEBRATION	ISBN#1-55698 330-1
TREK: THE DEEP SPACE CREW BOOK	ISBN#1-55698-335-2
TREK: THE ENCYCLOPEDIA	ISBN#1-55698-331-X

TO ORDER CALL TOLL FREE: (800)444-2524 ext. 67
credit cards happily accepted

Library of Congress Cataloging-in-Publication Data
James Van Hise, 1959—

   Let's Trek: The Budget Traveller's Guide to The Federation Worlds

   1.   Let's Trek: The Budget Traveller's Guide to The Federation Worlds

        (television, popular culture)
 I. Title

Published by Pioneer Books, Inc., 5715 N. Balsam Rd., Las Vegas, NV, 89130.

First Printing, 1994

PUBLISHER, EDITOR, DESIGNER: Hal Schuster
COVER ART BY Bruce Wood, COVER DESIGN BY Hal Schuster
All interior photographs ©1994 Albert L. Ortega

LET'S TREK

The Budget Traveller's Guide to

Federation Worlds

Traveling is fraught with difficulties both big and small. This book, while examining the main aspects of numerous worlds in the Federation (and a few outside), offers tips and guides to what makes a world interesting and what makes it necessary to avoid.

Those worlds that do not list specifically recommended hotels have the standard Best Traveler and Galactic Inn chains found on numerous Federation worlds, along with the Hyatt Regency, Hilton, Holiday Inn and Howard Johnson chains that virtually span the galaxy. Some worlds have very special inns and hotels particular in style and approach to that world, and those are singled out. Yonada is one example that has one of the most renowned Klingon restaurants in the Alpha Quadrant!

The history of a world is mentioned when important events have affected how that world has met the challenge of facing the future to become a modern, progressive planet.

Gamma Canaris N-Worlds shrouded in rumor and innuendo are examined and the facts are laid out to shatter any myths, such as with Rutia IV. Some worlds, such as Risa, are examined in greater detail due to their special popularity as travel centers.

Which worlds are travel friendly and which are not? This book gives all the facts. The "Forbidden Worlds" are listed to insure that your vacation isn't cut short by an extended stay in a Federation penal colony for violating Prime Directive restrictions or by visiting a world where the inhabitants are likely to eat any tourists they encounter.

The Alpha Quadrant offers a vast array of worlds and this book examines more than 125 of them. Heard of a planet but can't remember what it offers as special features? This book tells you. Does the planet have a certain historical event worth noting? We won't keep you in the dark. And why is Risa considered a favored shore leave world? Look and see!

What about those worlds you'll never get to visit, like Romulus and Cardassia? You can visit as an armchair traveler. We'll clue you in on those, and then you won't feel sorry that you're not going there.

Even that dark delight Klinzai—the Klingon homeworld—is examined in detail. We tell you everything you ever wanted to know about Klingons, but were afraid to ask a Klingon about directly.

A NOTE TO OUR READERS

The information for this book is gathered by researchers during the late spring and summer months. Each listing is derived from the assigned researcher's opinion based upon his or her visit at a particular time. The opinions are expressed in a candid and forthright manner. Other travellers might disagree. Those travelling at a different time may have different experiences since prices, dates, hours, and conditions are always subject to change. You are urged to check beforehand to avoid inconvenience and surprises. Travel always involves a certain degree of risk, especially in low-cost areas. When travelling, especially on a budget, you should always take particular care to insure your safety.

Travel Tips

The first time traveler, especially one from a planet with little off-world traffic, will be astounded by the variety of unusual people that populate the galaxy. A few simple tips will guide the new traveler dealing with aliens for the first time:

Always mind your manners.

Never assume your manners are the alien's manners.

Always keep your eyes and your mind open.

Here's a quick survey of some of the non-Federation aliens.

EXTREME INDIVIDUALS The peoples of the galaxy vary greatly.

The Halkans are pacifists, among the most agreeable people in the galaxy. Don't be fooled by their pleasant manners. They will refuse to budge on a point of principle. They refuse to export dilithium crystals to the Federation, even though they are plentiful on their world.

The Ferengi are avaricious. It is almost impossible to avoid Ferengi merchants and con men.

There continue to be many conflicts in space. The Tellarians, a patriarchal species with strong family units, recently ended a war against the Federation. The honorable species rescues stranded travelers. They are hospitable in a brusque way, but their accommodations are severe and their food bland. They adopt abandoned children of other species, and are clearly not xenophobic.

Cardassians may be encountered near Bajor and the Denorios Belt. They engaged in a long war with the Federation until an armistice was signed and the Cardassians withdrew from Bajor. It is a fragile peace. Travelers encountering Cardassian vessels are advised to avoid all contact. Cardassians encountered on Federation worlds are not a threat, although often arrogant and overbearing. Cardassians in contact with the Federation are members of the military; their personality may not be representative of all Cardassians. Cardassians are a warrior race, colder and more calculating than Klingons, and thus potentially more dangerous. Recent intelligence reports reveal a growing anti-militarism that the Cardassian High Command is attempting to crush.

UNLIKELY POSSIBILITIES Some rarely sighted galactic civilizations are almost mythical. The Douwd may have reality-altering mental powers. Reputed to be similar to the Q in abilities, they do not share that race's interest in Terrans.

Little is known of the origins and motivations of the "Q." One is notorious for frequent intrusions into Federation affairs. He has referred to a "Q Continuum," leading to expostulation that they dwell in a parallel dimension that borders on our own. They may be energy beings in their natural state. The species seems to be testing humanity, but their motivations are unknown.

Some species offer little basis for communication. The distant Shelius star system is the home to a race known as the Sheliak Corporate. The crystalline life forms speak a completely unknown language. They have grasped the basics of several Federation languages, enough to agree to the Treaty of Armens after one hundred and eleven years of entreaties. They have never met with Federation emissaries in person, so their general appearance remains unknown.

RECLUSIVE AND ELUSIVE The Jarada, or Harada, are an insectoid species possessed of a complex language. History records that the first Federation ambassador to contact them incorrectly pronounced a greeting. The greeting was simple to the Jarada, but mind-numbingly complex to humanoids. The Jarada were so offended they withdrew from contact for decades, finally agreeing to another diplomatic approach after ignoring all Federation messages for years. Fortunately, Captain Jean-Luc Picard of the USS Enterprise mastered the greeting, and so a limited diplomatic exchange with the Jarada has finally begun. The Grizellas, another far-flung species, are even more approachable— although since they hibernate six months out of their year (which is close to a standard Terran revolution) it might be necessary to time a visit properly. They are a party to the Treaty of Armens, distant neighbors of the Sheliak Corporate.

There are rumors and legends of species few believe exist. In the case of the planet Aldea, the myths turned out to be essentially true. A worldwide computerized shield concealed this planet located in the Epsilon Mynos system. The world suffers from nearly complete ozone depletion. Since the removal of the shield the Aldeans have become accessible to the outside universe. They are struggling to rebuild their population and welcome tourists and colonists.

The T'Kon Empire also turned out to be real. The ancient culture, which once ruled much of the Milky Way galaxy, has been extinct for six hundred thousand years. Underlining the mortality of civilizations, ruins can be found scattered on desolate, abandoned worlds.

ORIGINS OF THE GALACTIC PEOPLES Many humanoid races owe their existence to an incredibly ancient, greatly advanced, *ur*-humanoid species. The race seeded primordial oceans of many worlds with genetic codes. A single message from this species, the most ancient hologram known, has been deciphered. Their form and voice echoes across billions of years to address their descendants.

This race may be the Preservers, whose existence had previously been expostulated. Several worlds contain obviously transplanted human populations and protective devices beyond the technological capability of their inhabitants. The devices are designed to ward off dangers from space. The connection of the *ur*-humanoids to the Preservers is conjecture, and the artifacts of the Preservers are much more recent than the *ur*-humanoids are believed to be.

Recently, the Wadi, a race native to the Gamma Quadrant, passed through the Wormhole. The strange, mysterious, game-playing aliens are only one of the recent species to appear. The galaxy brims with new discoveries every day.

BLACK CLUSTERS This phenomenon was recently revealed. The easily detected clusters generate a powerful, destructive graviton wave front feedback in response to the presence of a starship's shields. This can be avoided by passing through the cluster with shields disengaged. Before this discovery, it was possible for a starship to suffer severe loss of life and even destruction from the graviton wave feedback. Black Clusters occur throughout the galactic rim.

The United Federation of Planets

The United Federation of Planets is the galaxy's largest association of worlds. It is dedicated to the equality of all galactic species and their cultures.

Primary requirements for membership include interstellar space fight and a non-oppressive, world government. Founded by Vulcan and several other worlds, the Federation welcomed Earth (AKA Terra) as a full member several centuries ago.

The central administration of the Federation is now located on Earth. The headquarters of Starfleet is also locate on Earth. It is the Federation's space fleet dedicated to exploration, cultural contact and scientific research.

EXTREME INDIVIDUALS Terrans is among the most widespread of Federation species. Terrans refer to their kind as "humans." In an amusing if anachronistic throwback to pre-contact days of planetary isolation, they refer to most other similar species as "humanoid." Although generally an agreeable species, humans often let their emotions reign unchecked.

VULCANS Vulcans learn to control their emotions. They are best recognized by their height, pointed ears and arched eyebrows. They rank among the greatest scientists of the Federation. (See "Vulcan")

ANDORIANS Andorians are best recognized by their blue skin, wild white hair and the pair of short, knobby antennae. Once a warlike race, their now subdued manners conceal a potential for violent action.

Andorians reproduce rapidly. Because of growing population, Andorians actively seek colonization of other worlds.

The fractious Federation race is often involved in territorial disputes. They avoid conflicts with Romulans, Klingons and Cardassians. They have been censured by the Federation on numerous occasions, largely because of ongoing pointless disagreements with the Tellarites.

BOLIANS These humanoid Federation members inhabitant the planet Bolius Nine. They look human but are hairless, with light bluish-green skin and a slight but distinct skull ridge.

Many Bolians serve in Starfleet. Renowned gossips, they are otherwise quite admirable and can adapt to any new situation. First time space travelers meeting Bolians are often surprised at the pronounced personality change between a first meeting and later, more relaxed, encounters.

TELLARITES Tellarites, although humanoid, have faces similar to Earth pigs. They are constantly involved in petty, heated conflicts with Andorians.

Tellarites are noted for having the worst dining habits and personal manners of any Federation race. If a Tellarite insults you, don't take it personally— they're rude to everybody.

FEDERATION

TRILL The sophisticated Trill look like Terrans except for a faint pattern of dark skin spots. The spots, which vary between individuals, run down the temple, neck and shoulders. Many Trill have slight nose ridges.

Some Trill serve as hosts for an intelligent, sluglike species that shares their world. The honor is reserved for the most brilliant Trill. This symbiotic relationship produces a merging of minds, personality and knowledge.

The symbionts live several centuries. It is possible to meet a Trill possessing the accumulated knowledge and experience of many lifetimes.

It is possible to meet the same person in different bodies. The "new' Trill is both the old Trill and a new personality. This hosts can even differ in gender.

Trills have remarkably good manners, and excel as diplomats and scientists. Trills are among the most loyal of species.

PLACES

Besides the home planets of the Federation, there are many colonies and other places of interest. For example, while the Federation outpost at Bersallis Three is fairly small, the planet is the site of spectacular firestorms. A short side trip is more than worthwhile, as long as weather conditions haven't forced evacuation.

Visitor's to Sherman's Planet might be interested in a quick jaunt to Space Station K-7, a decommissioned station housing a small museum. The museum is dedicated to an early encounter with Klingons, known to history buffs as the Tribble Incident.

The frontier spirit survives on many worlds. Cestus III, still a desolate, sparsely populated planet, is the location of a lonely monument to pioneers killed by the Gorn over a century ago.

On a lighter note, visitors pay brief visits to the scenic wonders of Omicron Ceti III. Although plagued by Berthold rays, the planet is home to an airborne spore that, when inhaled, provides immunity to the deadly radiation. Early colonies were forced to relocate when the spores produced a euphoric state that made it impossible to pursue any goal beyond pleasure and relaxation. Work was ignored.

Now the site of a small atmosphere and radiation-shielded research center, Omicron Ceti III is accessible again thanks to a hypospray that suppresses the spores negative effects.

Regulations prevent visitors, or staff, from spending more than three hours outside the shielded areas. Grim reminders of the past crop up everywhere: Tantalus V maintains a dismal reputation as the site of the last Federation penal colony.

The indigenous inhabitants, the Horta, are a silicon-based life form who work in unison with human miners. This may be the only known self-regenerating mineral resource in the galaxy.

It is a rare example of humanoid and non-humanoid collaboration. The cooperation almost took a tragic turn in the early years of the settlement. The Horta, once on the verge of extinction, now flourish, as does the mineral industry of Janus VI.

SCHOLARLY PURSUITS

Scholars and tourists find much of interest at Memory Alpha. The small planetoid houses the central information archive of the United Federation of Planets. It is home for all known information.

Complete historical data of every Federation member world is stored here, as is all available information about the culture and science of all other known planets.

Stored scientific knowledge includes everything from biology to archaeology, from subdimensional physics to infrastellar dynamics. It can be accessed by anyone.

Memory Alpha is dedicated to the freedom of information. Some classified Starfleet data may be excluded, of course.

This sight was severely damaged shortly after birth a century ago. It was extensively rebuilt and has since operated without incident.

The Federation world Pacifica is almost entirely covered with water. Ground-based cultures, predominantly Terran, easily adapted to this aquatic locale.

Pacifica's amazing array of ocean life, none of which is restrained or captured by the colonists, is a wonder to behold; at least one species is believed to be sentient. This has yet to be conclusively proven. Research continues, and can be followed at the Visitor's Bureau of the Pacifica Indigenous Life Research Lab in Aquatic Sector 23-ALZ.

Zedak Four is also a water planet. Colonists cluster on and around the world's few land masses. They do not live completely on the water.

Access to Parliament, the site of top-level Federation diplomatic conferences, is restricted to individuals of diplomatic rank. Rumor has it there's not much to see.

Ramatis Three is noted for its magnificent stone architecture, which rivals that of Earth's ancient Greek and Byzantine empires. The elite class on this world is bred for special mental powers. A side effect renders them incapable of speech.

The telepaths communicate through three other members of their species, who serve as a "chorus" translating their thoughts and feelings into words. Riva, the famed Federation negotiator, was one such individual.

HAZARDS OF SPACE

Travelers should be aware that space travel is dangerous. Advanced spacecraft have not changed that simple fact.

Planets can also be dangerous. The Federation colony on Delta Rana IV suffered complete devastation. All eleven thousand inhabitants were killed by an attack from space launched by the mysterious race known as the Husnock. Once a lushly forested planet, it is now a barren shell orbited by three lifeless moons. It may never be fit for habitation again.

Recently, the Borg invaded Federation space, causing great property damage and the loss of many lives. The first Federation encounter with the Borg occurred nearly three years (at maximum warp) from Starbase 185. They caught Federation Starfleet forces off guard.

The MS One Colony and the Federation civilian outpost at Ohniaka Three were destroyed. It is believed that the earlier destruction of the Neutral Zone border outpost

FEDERATION

Delta 0-5 was caused by a Borg scouting expedition into Federation space. The Borg were finally defeated at Wolf 359.

The outer regions of Federation space have often been the scene of hostile encounters. Sector 9569 marks the region of the only known Federation encounter with the Zalkonians. Sector 23 contains the border with the Romulan Neutral Zone; safety prevents virtually all tourist traffic.

Starbase Zendi Nine is located in a safer region, the mooring site of the USS Stargazer, a relic of the Battle of Maxia. This battle was the only official hostile action between the Ferengi and the Federation. It is light years away from the site of the battle, a set of coordinates in empty space containing very little to see.

Some hazards apply only to the outer regions of Federation space. There are many worlds to explore in safer, more central regions. Frontier regions are relatively safe, and the pleasures of a trip to Bajor, Deep Space Nine, and the Gamma Quadrant Wormhole far outweigh any minor risk.

Starfleet provides security in most outer regions. The Federation is dedicated to interplanetary peace, and to cultural and scientific exchange. There is no more amenable region of the galaxy.

Traveler Alert

Statistically it is easier to drown in your own bathtub than to be killed in space travel. With this in mind, the traveler should still be aware that a number of species and cultures have been hostile and destructive. It is important to avoid contact with spacecraft from these cultures and other menaces.

The predatory Crystalline Entity is an immense sentient being that draws its sustenance from the energy of entire worlds. It has been destroyed, but there is the risk that one or more others may exist. Fortunately, a means of communicating with it was devised. Any being of this sort should be avoided at all costs, regarded as destructive, and reported immediately.

OTHER ENTITIES TO WATCH OUT FOR

The tall, reptilian Gorn have green, scaly skin. They have not been encountered for nearly a century. That encounter destroyed the Federation settlement on Cestus III. Gorn are hostile to all other species, extremely territorial, and devoid of regard for non-Gorn sentient life.

Tholians are an extremely reclusive alien culture that avoids all other species. Encounters are rare. Vulcan archives record that the Tholians simply wish to be left alone.

These isolationists will attack with unusual strategies when their space is intruded upon. The insectoids have a well-deserved reputation as brilliant military minds, but they are peaceful when left alone.

They destroyed a Starbase without any warning. Travelers who venture into their space by mishap may be given an opportunity to withdraw immediately. All are advised to take the opportunity to flee if given.

Melkots, also known as Melkotians, are also isolationists. They react to unwanted visitors with arbitrary cruelty. Fortunately they stay on their home planet. The approach to their world is clearly marked by warning buoys several light years distant. It is highly unlikely you will meet them anywhere else.

CAUTION MUST PREVAIL

Little is known of the Husnock, destroyers of the Federation colony on Rana IV. This was the only known encounter with this advanced, space faring race. They are a complete mystery. Their appearance is unknown, as no trace of them is visible in the wake of an attack.

It is not advisable to visit Soleis V at this time. The famed Federation mediator Riva is currently working with local tribes to end the civil wars. It remains a hostile environment for travelers.

A traveler should always be cautious when approaching any unknown space faring vessel. Even a Klingon ship can be a potential threat, as there are renegades who regard the current state of alliance between their Empire and the Federation as shameful.

There are also the Ferengi. Some Ferengi are pirates.

Although no state of declared conflict exists between the Federation and the Romulans, it is best to regard Romulans as hostile.

Reports of Cardassian treaty and humanoid rights violations are well documented. Proceed with caution.

These few pointers should help you keep out of serious trouble. Remember them, stay within approved travel routes, and your galactic tour will not only be pleasant, it will be trouble-free.

BORG

AVOID ALL CONTACT
PREDATORY ALIEN SPECIES
REPORT ALL SIGHTINGS IMMEDIATELY— PRIORITY ONE!
No one needs warning about the Borg. Although sightings have been rare since their defeat at Wolf 359, travelers are advised to avoid them at all costs. Immediately alert local authorities of any encounter.

Travelers must take cover in the unlikely event they encounter representatives of this utterly alien hive-culture. Their appearance is familiar in the aftermath of the Battle of Wolf 359. Since they were repelled at great cost during this encounter, they have made no further incursions into civilized regions. There is no indication that the Klingons, Romulans or Cardassians have encountered them of late.

There was an unconfirmed encounter between the Federation and a Borg vessel a year ago. However, Starfleet denies this.

The location of the Borg home world, if there is one, is unknown. It appears that they originate hundreds of light years from our region of the galaxy. They may live only in their roaming hive-ships.

The mysterious destruction of science outpost Delta-Five, and other Federation and Romulan outposts along the Neutral Zone, show many indications of a Borg attack, but these occurred before the Borg were known.

A member of the Q Continuum caused the Federation flagship, the Enterprise, to be cast into System J-25. There it encountered a Borg craft, and only narrowly escaped. J-25 may be the location of the Borg homeworld.

All Borg ships known to date are immense cubes of space borne metal layered with randomly placed conduits and pipes. A Borg vessel is regenerative, able to recover from sustained damage in a remarkably brief time. Offensive capacities are incredibly advanced, far beyond the destructive or defensive capacities of Federation weapons technology.

The encounter with the Enterprise alerted the Borg to the existence of the Federation, which has proved disastrous.

The Borg are humanoid cyborgs. Portions of their natural bodies have been replaced by mechanical interfaces and extensions. Investigations indicate that the Borg are born as completely organic humanoids, but start alterations shortly after birth.

All Borg are part of the group mind. They believe this hive-mind state is the highest form of existence. They conduct raids to absorb energy from destroyed settlements and

TRAVELER ALERT

assimilate other species. They have destroyed at least one planet's inhabitants.

The Borg recently turned their attention to Federation space. The destruction of the New Providence Colony on Jouret IV was the first sign of their approach. This was their second encounter with the Enterprise, this time specifically to abduct and assimilate its captain, Jean-Luc Picard.

Armed with Picard's knowledge, the Borg cube headed to Earth, destroying all opposition in its path. The final battle came at Wolf 359. The Borg destroyed thirty-five Starfleet vessels, including the Saratoga, the Gage, the Kyushu, the Melbourne and the Tolstoi, before the Enterprise (under the command of William T. Riker) halted them in their tracks. This ended the mass destruction that fateful day, Stardate 44002.3, almost the last day of Earth's existence.

Recently, the Enterprise encountered the Borg twice more. First an injured, young Borg, nicknamed "Hugh" by the starship crew, was taken aboard. This Borg was exposed to human individuality before being returned to its companions in accordance with the Prime Directive.

A later encounter demonstrated that "Hugh's" experience had affected all the Borg on his ship. They had become confused by developing individual personalities. They are still potentially dangerous, and should be avoided at all costs.

It is not known whether Hugh has affected Borg other than those on his ship. Official warnings remain in effect and should be taken very seriously.

FORBIDDEN ZONES

Some worlds and systems are off-limits to all but authorized Starfleet personnel. In one case, Talos IV, no one is permitted contact. Violations will be treated very seriously. Even non-Federation signatories can face stiff penalties should they later apply for admission to the Federation or wish to engage in commerce with any Federation aligned planet.

BREKKA AND ORNARA The planets Ornara and Brekka, in the Delos System, are considered off limits by reason of the Prime Directive. The entire population of Ornara is addicted to Felicium, a drug supplied by their neighboring planet, Brekka.

Brekka trades the drug to Ornara in return for natural resources. The Ornarans believe they require the drug to fight an ancient plague that would otherwise ravage their world. The Brekkans know the disease was cured generations ago but take advantage of the Ornarans. They have deliberately addicted them to Felicium.

The Ornarans die without regular doses of Felicium, but believe the deaths are caused by the plague. The Brekkan civilization will eventually collapse since no one there understands the technology left from years before and the Ornarans only provide natural resources. As Brekkan ships begin to break down they can no longer continue to deliver the Felicium on schedule.

Neither world is a Federation member. It was determined Starfleet must follow the non-interference directive. If either world requests help from the Federation, a hearing will be convened. Only authorized representatives of the Federation are allowed contact with either world.

CAPELLA IV PRIME DIRECTIVE RESTRICTIONS APPLY

This small planet is rich in the mineral Topaline, formerly used in life support systems. Artificial substitutes have recently been found.

This beautiful world is covered with a greenish-blue flora visible from space that forms a stark contrast to scarlet oceans. The world has never been colonized or otherwise exploited by the Federation.

The primitive people of Capella IV are a pre-industrial culture that would be contaminated by outside contact. The isolationist Capellans live in tribes and fight wars with armaments such as the Kligat, a three-bladed weapon particularly destructive in close quarters.

Before the Klingon/Federation Alliance, the Klingons attempted to infiltrate this culture to establish a trading outpost. A Federation force expelled them. Following the Alliance, the Klingons reluctantly accepted sanctions for their interference with Capella IV. Observation teams have studied residual contamination for 80 years.

Capella IV must be kept free of contact for the foreseeable future.

DREMA IV PRIME DIRECTIVE RESTRICTIONS APPLY

This world in the Selcundi Drema system is the location of the most massive deposit of dilithium crystals ever discovered. The world remains off limits to mining because this is a pre space flight culture and has not yet experienced a first contact. The Prime Directive has been invoked to prevent cultural contamination.

The humanoid beings of Drema IV should make first contact in the next century. The world will then benefit from its dilithium deposits.

The dilithium deposits have effected Drema IV by forming lattices that caused geological instabilities. A Federation starship discovered these anomalies and used its phaser banks to relieve the threat to the civilization on that world. Drone survey ships continue to monitor the planet from a high orbit that makes them undetectable to the people on Drema IV.

ENNIS CAUTION: PRISON WORLD—AVOID AT ALL COSTS
DO NOT ATTEMPT LANDING EVEN IN DIRE EMERGENCY

Located one third of a light year from the Bajoran Wormhole, Ennis is one of the few documented inhabited worlds in the Gamma Quadrant. Ennis is not a natural planet, but an artificial satellite prison. The official reports of Commander Benjamin Sisko remain the only concrete information available.

The prisoners of Ennis come from two opposed factions on their home world. The two groups— the Ennis and the Nol-Ennis— kill each other in endless battles. An artificial microbe in the atmosphere prevents inmates from dying. Instead they awaken the next day to resume the pointless struggle.

Golin Shel-la is chief of the Ennis side. His counterpart, Zlangco, leads the Nol-Ennis. A third party, the Kai Opaka, the former Bajoran religious leader, opted to live on Ennis when he was infected with the microbe. He tries to help the inhabitants.

Security on this barbarous prison world makes it impossible to discover how her efforts are proceeding. It is a great irony of space travel that this source of immortality in the Gamma Quadrant is more of a curse than a blessing.

Federation warning beacons make the approach to Ennis difficult. No one has even tried to go there. This Federation restricted world is not one of the scenic wonders of the universe.

GAMMA TRIANGULI VI This world is forming its own culture after centuries of living under the benevolent subjugation of the computer, Vaal. Vaal controlled the weather on this world and insured that the simple people could grow food without fear of droughts and storms. The computer also kept the people ignorant and culture stagnated.

When James T. Kirk and the Enterprise destroyed Vaal they launched this people on the road to civilization. A century later, they continue to work towards space flight and first contact with a Federation peoples.

The Prime Directive has been invoked and Gamma Trianguli VI is off limits to other worlds. The Federation has secret outposts on this world, just as on Mintaka and others. They observe life among these simple people and secretly protect them from off world cultural contamination.

A deadly plant which aims and hurls thorns inhabits this planet. The thorns contain a very potent poison known as Saplin, a toxin counteracted only by the drug Masiform D.

ICONIA This planet is located near the Romulan Neutral Zone. Approach by anyone in the Federation may be viewed as a violation of the armistice agreement with the Romulans. The neutral zone was established more than 200 years ago.

Romulans displayed no interest in this cold piece of stone until a Starfleet survey team made an important archeological discovery several years ago. The world has been devoid of life since a war more than 200 thousand years ago.

This is the homeworld of the extinct Iconians. They possessed instantaneous transportation when most worlds now in the Federation were populated by primitives. This technology survived the obliteration of the Iconians, but has not been transferred off that cold world due to a dispute with the Romulans.

The Iconian transporter, the "Gateway," creates a portal a traveler can use to observe or reach his destination. The portal is invisible and undetectable until the traveler steps through. It is a completely different system than the modern transporter beam.

A strange satellite, the "Iconian Probe," exists near the world. It can cause disable starships. Numerous hazards exist for those who approach this seemingly dead world.

MALKOR PRIME DIRECTIVE RESTRICTIONS APPLY
This class M world is much like Earth at the beginning of the 21st century. The humanoid Malkorians are not yet members of the Federation. Most Malkorians are unaware of the Federation.

This world is off-limits due to General Order Number One. Interference with inhabitants is strictly forbidden.

Should you find yourself on this world, be aware that many natives are xenophobic. If you are stranded, disguise yourself as a Malkorian.

The government conspires to keep people unaware of the existence of alien life forms so you must put yourself in government hands and hope they are trustworthy. This might be a dangerous route since reports indicate that branches of the government do not agree about aliens. Some only want to keep them secret from the populace while others see them as a threat. The latter might not be adverse to murder. Stay away from this planet.

The Malkorians had a violent past, but are now at peace. They will soon have a warp drive. When this happens, they will be invited to join the Federation.

When this world opens to outsiders, tourism should flourish. Malkorians have a lot to offer, from literature to theatre, to magnificent art that graces their museums and colleges. They are developing a highly culture. More will be learned about this world when it opens to outsiders.

MINOS This dead planet in the Lorenz Cluster is home to an automated device left by an extinct civilization. The device still tries to sell armaments to passing ships.

The device demonstrates the effectiveness of its wares on anyone visiting Minos. The weapons already destroyed the entire civilization of that planet. It is recommended that no one visit this world.

The starship Enterprise was almost destroyed when it discovered this planet. Minos is off-limits to all visitors. Federation scientists study the technology under secret clearance. Official Starfleet permission is needed to approach the world.

Little is known of Minosian civilization, only that Minos was once a desert-world, much like Vulcan today. It had small salt seas and vast tributaries of underground, fresh water springs and streams.

Minos has no life, though it did once. Its barren remains are unattractive to all but miners who hope eventually to attain mineral and salvage rights. This world may be rich in diamonds, silver and nickel. Trititanium has also been reported to be in abundance.

MINTAKA III This world is home to the Mintakans—proto-Vulcans with a Bronze Age culture. This planet is currently off-limits to all travelers. Visiting violates General Order Number One, the Prime Directive of non-interference. Inhabitants are vulnerable to outside influence and superstitious in nature.

Their lyzome levels prevent the standard Federation mind-erasing technique from working. This is used when a culture has accidentally been contaminated. When the starship Enterprise investigated this world, unintentional interference caused the Mintakans to believe captain Jean-Luc Picard is a god. This is exactly what the Prime Directive is designed to prevent. Starfleet does not wish to see their people worshipped as gods by any life forms.

Mintakans are a peaceful people. Interference with this world is dangerous only to the inhabitants. Outsiders need not fear these gentle, proto-Vulcanoid beings should this planet open up for tourism in the distant future.

Mintaka is a desert, rocky world with two major salt oceans and a scattering of land-locked fresh-water lakes. Temperature ranges from below freezing at the poles to 130 degrees Fahrenheit at the equator. Wildlife includes the hornbuck, an animal hunted for food and clothing by the Mintakans.

Thousands of animal species live on this world. Mintaka is rich in ore deposits, and has a large cache of dilithium. Mining on this world is banned. Mintakans will eventually decide if they wish to mine and trade their planet's resources.

Mintakans are thought to be of Vulcan/Romulan origin, brought to the planet 5000 years ago. It is not known whether the Preservers or another advanced race caused this 'seeding' of Vulcanian and humanoid cultures throughout the galaxy.

NEURAL Outside interference has led to a rapidly growing civilization on this world. During the last 80 years, inhabitants graduated from a tribal, 17th century North American Earth-like culture to a society with rockets and two-dimensional television. This world is off-limits due to the non-interference directive, Starfleet's General Order Number One.

The world should soon discover warp drive. Neuralians are intelligent but, if not for the illegal interference by both Klingons and Starfleet 80 years ago, would not be so quickly advancing their civilization. This quick advancement has caused many large wars. Xeno-anthropologists predict they will survive and soon venture into the stars.

The Kanutu tribe on Neural heal with their minds. Rumor says they can control minds through herbs and telepathy, but this claim is unsubstantiated.

They are highly regarded by the peoples of Neural. Their advanced knowledge of herbs and roots is considered a highly regarded scientific specialty.

Wildlife is deadly, especially the Mugato, a shaggy, albino creature with a single horn protruding from the center of its forehead. It resembles an Earth gorilla, mates for life, and is very territorial. Its bite is poisonous, and it has been known to attack people. The mahko-root, used in conjunction with the mental powers of the Kanutu healers, is the only known antidote.

Neural is a class M world with forests, mountains, deserts, salt oceans and fresh water lakes. Like Miri, it is remarkably Earth-like. The people are completely human in appearance. Scientists believe they may be another lost human tribe. When the planet opens for visitors in the near future, it should be fascinating.

RIGEL VII PRIME DIRECTIVE RESTRICTIONS APPLY

Do not confuse Rigel VII with the shore leave world in this solar system. The Federation has declared the world off limits until the violent native tribes are no longer a threat. The Federation is concerned they may achieve space flight and spread their cruelty to other worlds.

Rigelians can accomplish this on their own. The Prime Directive prohibits interference and the Federation will not tolerate profiteering off-worlders to sell technology to these tribes. Anyone caught attempting to sell advanced technology to Rigel VII will be sentenced to life on a prison planet with no possibility of parole.

Beings from worlds not aligned with the Federation who attempt to sell advanced technology to the Rigelians will find that the Federation considers this an act of war. Thus far no one has attempted to defy the Federation restriction. Even the Romulans and Cardassians realize the Rigelians hold loyalty only for those within their own tribes.

RUBICAM III A forbidden world initially regarded as a perfect shore leave planet. Hedonistic and gregarious inhabitants of this world are called the Edo. They enjoy visitors, are sexually adventurous and explore the limits in everything they do, particularly in play.

This lush, green Class M world is ruled by a mysterious orbital "god" device. The origin of this omnipotent satellite is unknown. It exists partially in our dimension and dwarfs the might of a starship.

This "Edo Lord" protects the planet and its people but rules with an iron will. The laws are simple and few, but even the most minor violation results in instant death. The world is crime free, but mistakes are not forgiven.

During the first contact with a Federation vessel several years ago, a cadet was almost executed for stepping on a flower in a protected zone. Only an appeal to the Edo Lord's intelligence saved him. Until the Federation knows more about the Edo Lord and believes minor infractions will not result in summary executions, Rubicam III will be off limits.

SHA KA REE The renegade Vulcan, Sybok, discovered this planet 75 years ago. He twisted ancient legends to insist this world located in the heart of a vast cosmic barrier was the origin point of life and the home of the creator. There was an ancient being on this world but, like Armus and The Gorgon, the creature had been imprisoned for crimes against life. The powerful being was destroyed by the disrupters of a Klingon warbird.

This didn't remove all threats. Primitive living rock men are also an on-going threat to visitors. This harsh, cold desert planet is not pleasant to visit.

Important questions remain as to whether this planet is indeed the Sha Ka Ree of legend. The name has stuck. No other "Sha Ka Ree" has been discovered in the known universe.

Only a Galaxy Class Starship or a Klingon bird-of-prey has a chance of making it through the cosmic barrier that surrounds this planet. The world is unlikely to ever be deemed safe for casual visitors.

Some insist the Federation is hiding something on this world, but the logs of the Enterprise-A are freely accessible to all media. Nothing is held back.

Several Klingon vessels have penetrated the barrier exploring this world on their own. They returned with tales of great battles and violent deaths against armored beings with flesh like stone. The Klingons found it a glorious world with many opportunities for violent personal combat. The Federation raised no complaint since the Klingons are capable of defending themselves and know what to expect.

No Prime Directive restrictions apply to this planet, but it is dangerous and should be avoided by all but authorized Starfleet personnel.

TALOS IV GENERAL ORDER SEVEN
(NO CONTACT UNDER ANY CIRCUMSTANCES)

This world was discovered more than a century ago by Starfleet officer Captain Christopher Pike. General Order Seven has prohibited all contact ever since. Violation of this order is the only crime under Federation law that is punishable by death.

This is the fourth planet in the Talos star group, a dual star system with a total of eleven planets. The surface of this Class M planet is desert comparable to that in the American southwest on Earth.

Ages ago the people of this world destroyed their civilization in an atomic war. Survivors will remain in shelters deep beneath the planet's surface until the surface radiation is low enough for them to safely live in the sunlight again.

Their culture had developed limited space flight, but the Talosians believe they have a unique link to their world. The few sojourns off-world were to capture specimens for experiments. These experiments consume so much time there is no attempt to overcome their homing instinct.

The humanoid Talosians are less than two meters in height and have a large skull cavity. This greater brain capacity proved to be their undoing.

Talosians are hermaphroditic, bearing male and female characteristics. This enabled the few survivors to reproduce. Their mammoth brains demand new frontiers to explore.

Living below ground in a network of tunnels and caverns gives most Talosians claustrophobia. They tap alien species' memories and repeatedly relived them. Dozens of Talosians experienced the same memory hyperillusion simultaneously.

Captured species provided a memory bank of opportunities for Talosians to escape the tedium of their underground lives. Plans for moving back to the surface were abandoned as new beings were sought to add memories to the Talosian archives.

A DYING RACE The Talosians allowed their technology to fall into disrepair as they relived lives more exciting than their own. Talosians never attempted to experience things first hand. Time passed as they lived in hyperdreams and awakened only to eat before returning to the memory vault. Some forgot to set alarms and slowly starved to death as they dreamed.

When a Federation ship crashed on Talos IV, the Talosians nursed the sole survivor, a young woman, back to health. Captain Pike and his landing party were then lured to Talos IV by a fake distress call. Pike was taken prisoner as a potential mate for the Earth woman, Vina.

The Talosians decided to return to the surface so the humans could reproduce and provide new minds to be probed. Of course, the children would only have memories of life on Talos IV, devoid of excitement. Unfortunately for the Talosians, humans detest captivity. Pike and his team were willing to die rather than help enslave future generations.

The Talosians believed human beings too violent a species for their purposes and allowed them to leave. Since then Talos IV has been ruled off limits. Satellites monitor Talos IV to keep Talosians in and visitors out. There are few remaining inhabitants.

TAU CYGNA V This former site of a Federation colony has been declared off limits under the Treaty of Armens. The Sheliak Corporate and the Federation agreed that according to paragraph seven in section 133, humans living on the colony on Tau Cygna V were in violation of treaty. According to section 502, paragraph 716, subparagraph 5, "Unwanted humans on H Class planets may be removed at the discretion of the Sheliak Corporate."

The colony ship Artemis had crashed on this world when it veered off course. Although hyperonic radiation killed a third of the colonists, the rest adapted and built a primitive but comfortable outpost.

When the Sheliak Corporate protested the presence of the colony, the Federation had no choice but to use force to relocate the stubborn colonists. It is unknown what the Sheliak Corporate has since done with this world. They do not welcome uninvited visitors.

TERELLA Biological warfare rendered this planet uninhabitable. Nobody won when the world was left a deadly breeding ground for a plague that wiped out most of the population.

Survivors fled in spaceships. No inhabited world would allow them to land. The survivors carry a plague virus that will infect anyone they meet.

Terella "plague ships" are destroyed when they are recognized by any race familiar with their history. Every planet knows the horrors that ravaged Terella and will do anything to prevent the same from happening to their own world. Only a handful of "plague ships" still exist, wandering the galaxy, looking for safe haven to live out their lives.

Terella is infested with plague and must be thoroughly decontaminated by exterminating all life. Reluctant to implement this policy, the Federation is investigating alternatives. Meanwhile a complete quarantine is in effect. A network of monitoring satellites insures that approaching vessels are warned away.

TILONUS IV A temporary ban on travel to this world has been instituted until further notice. Civil unrest makes this world unsafe for travelers. Visitors have been attacked or imprisoned. The rebels use mind probes on tourists.

After the kidnapping of a Federation officer, the advisory warning was changed to a ban. The Federation has warned Tilonus IV that severe reprisals will result if a visitor is molested.

TURKANA IV Civilization on this planet collapsed 30 years ago. Its people wage constant war. They have rejected offers of assistance from the Federation.

The opposing sides, the Coalition and the Alliance, wear implants to alert them when enemies are near. A sneak attack is difficult and battles can sometimes be avoided.

Some inhabitants have fled their world, including the late Tasha Yar. The former security officer aboard the Enterprise grew up dodging roving rape gangs who hunt women and children.

Neither side will accept help from the Federation. Neither side trusts anyone with that much power. They fear Starfleet will move in and take over. They believe all off-worlders are Federation spies and will kill them on sight.

VAGRA II The evil entity calling itself Armus was exiled to this world in the Zed Lapis system. Armus killed a Starfleet officer, so the Federation wants to insure no others fall prey to this merciless creature.

The people who created Armus purged themselves of all evil by transferring it into this sludge-like being. Armus is only capable of hate for all beings. As the only intelligent being on this world, it is lonely and craves company.

Vagra II is a desolate planet. Even using this barren rock for emergency landings would be dangerous because of Armus.

VANDOR IV This world suffers after-effects of the time distortion experiments of Dr. Robert Manheim. Past and future overlap with devastating effects. No one knows which time period is the "present."

When the device was finally shut down, it had caused fractures in the time stream that have yet to be repaired or understood. Visitors have been banned until further notice.

Research teams from several Federation worlds live and work on Vandor IV. They study the phenomenon and map trouble spots. Time appears to be slowly resuming its normal shape. Vandor IV should be completely safe within 25 years Earth Standard.

VELARA III This world demonstrates what can go wrong when Terraformers are too eager and overlook test results. Velara III was declared devoid of indigenous life forms, perfect for terraforming in a part of the galaxy short of new worlds for colonization.

After the terraforming proceeded for five years, an indigenous, microscopic life form was discovered. It showed signs of collective intelligence. The Federation forced the terraformers to cease operations on Velara III.

The Prime Directive demands that indigenous life forms on any world be allowed to live and develop naturally. It makes this world off limits to visitors until further notice.

ZALKON This is a forbidden world in the Zeta Gelis Cluster. Zalkonians refuse to sign the basic human rights agreement the Federation extends to all worlds seeking diplomatic relations.

Zalkon is ruled by a fascist regime. The government uses violence and executions to silence political protest. It is presently undergoing a crisis to its existence.

Some Zalkons are experiencing a peculiar genetic metamorphosis in which a human being slowly changes into a disembodied entity. This entity will possess incredible powers.

When the Zalkon government discovers someone in the early stages of change, it executes them as a threat to the normal way of life. The Federation has offered sanctuary to Zalkonian refugees awaiting the completion of their metamorphosis.

It is not known how widespread this genetic change is within the population. Zalkon does not allow off-worlders to study the phenomenon.

It is believed that a majority of Zalkonians may undergo this change. If this is true, the fascist regime will collapse or a blood bath will ensue.

Worlds of the Federation

⊙ALFA 177

This is a desert planet mostly composed of rock and sand. It provides a harsh but beautiful home to the unicorn dog and other galactic wonders. Animal life is sparse and harmless.

Sunsets are among the most beautiful in the galaxy due to exotic ore deposits that emit invisible waves causing light refraction. This yellow ore is hazardous to all transporters. In extreme cases, the ore can cause the transporter to duplicate anything transported. The effect on living creatures is annoying if not deadly. The Federation Tourist Bureau insists tourists be transported to the surface of this world via shuttle or runabout. Federation law requires strict decontamination of tourists after their return from the world before they use a transporter.

RECOMMENDATIONS FOR TRAVELERS Temperature on this world is extreme, hot during the day, freezing within hours of sunset. High winds change the surface of the planet overnight. Resorts are located below the surface or under force fields to protect travelers from savage storms.

Humanoids should pack hot weather gear and cold weather gear. This is an ideal world for non-human campers of large bulk and thick exoskeleton not affected by temperature extremes. Primitive camping sites are available.

Rock climbing is a popular sport for humans and non-humans. The rare sighting of the gentle unicorn dog is said to bring good luck. This is a protected world and hunting is strictly forbidden.

Eighty percent of the resorts on Alfa 177 are run by Ferengi. Trade is encouraged in gold pressed latinum, but all known forms of currency are accepted, as well as credit cards. Indoor resorts offer a variety of entertainment, including gambling, fine restaurants, shopping and museums. A personal holo-suite may be requested and swimming is in heated, natural grotto pools. The pools are said to have healing properties, though scientists have not verified this Ferengi claim.

Alfa 177 resorts are listed as popular vacation spots in the TOURIST GUIDE FOR THE GALAXY'S RICH AND FAMOUS. Natural wonders include the heated underwater grottoes, Hanging Rock (not to be confused with Hanging Rock, Australia, Earth,) Venus Peak, the famous Box Coliseum and Mount Skull. These natural monuments rival even the giant natural pyramids of Mars and the stone labyrinths of Novachron.

ALDEA

The Federation recently learned of this world previously concealed by a cloaking device controlled by the Custodian. It is located in the Epsilon Mynos system.

ALDEA

The Custodian, a computer, governed this world for centuries, protecting it with a variety of devices. The system drained the planet's ozone layer, and Aldea is now subject to high doses of radiation that render most inhabitants sterile. The Tourist Bureau assists the humanoid Aldeans to encourage immigration. Only humanoids need apply.

Aldeans worked hard with their Custodian to build replace their natural ozone layer. Radiation levels decreased over the past few years.

Aldeans are fond of children, since they have few of their own. They built elaborate theme and amusement parks to entice young people from all over the galaxy to visit with their parents and, hopefully, remain as Aldean citizens.

The large, imaginative amusement parks are guaranteed safe by the Custodian. Elaborate rides include the Interdimensional Roller Coaster composed of invisible containment fields and tracks. Riders appear to fly. A containment field holds them firmly in place. Arms, legs and head remain free as the rider is driven to dizzying speeds and heights.

RECOMMENDATIONS FOR TRAVELERS Aldea is a paradise world of warm temperatures, beautiful, unpolluted beaches and friendly wildlife. Hazards are few. The Custodian keeps people safe from harm. There is virtually no crime. It is an ideal world on which to raise children.

Transportation is convenient. Transport from an orbiting ship is via the Custodian, the planetary transporter.

WHAT TO WATCH OUT FOR Aldea is still recovering from depletion of their ozone layer. Many adults suffer from medical problems. Medical care is good, but waiting lists are long because Aldea has a severe shortage of doctors.

Many Aldeans wish to adopt young, humanoid babies. Some have been known to 'borrow' other people's children. Travelers with young children are cautioned not to leave them unattended. The Custodian will insure a child is returned to the rightful parent. 'Borrowing' is frowned upon, but not illegal, although no permanent 'borrowing' has ever occurred. Aldeans want people to know their world is safe for all children.

Theme park rides are designed for humanoids only. Aldeans hope to expand to include rides for chlorine breathers, silicon-based rock creatures, gaseous anomaly beings and winged entities.

 **ALONDRA**

Seventy Earth standard years ago, this world was engulfed by a cosmic cloud and reduced to asteroid chunks. It no longer hosts tourists, though mining prospects are good. Mining claims should be filed with the Federation Land Acts department. Illegal mining brings strict penalties, including high fines and, in some cases, cryro incarceration.

 **ANDOR**

Andorians live on this beautiful world, located in the Epsilon Indi star system (also the home of anthropologist's delight, Triacus). The Andorians, despite a war-like reputation, welcome tourists. They are a mineral poor world deriving almost fifty percent of their planetary income from off-world vacationers.

Andor has much to offer! Black sand beaches and tossing green seas offer a luscious backdrop for any sunbather. Andor's gentle sun does not burn fair skin. Waves are strong enough to entice surfers, but gentle with virtually no dangerous riptides.

Andor's moons, Triptus and Daemon, are much smaller than Earth's single satellite. Their pull on the emerald waters is flowing and graceful. All water sports are available on Andor, from yachting to scuba-diving to water-walking. The drowned cities of ancient Andor offer a spectacle for scuba-divers. Andor is a sexually liberal planet with many adult, multi-alien entertainments to entice tourists. Gambling is legal.

RECOMMENDATIONS FOR TRAVELERS Andor is a warm planet. Winters are not harsh unless you are traveling to the extreme poles. The famous resorts, including Teliv By The Sea and Cape Ghost, are located in temperate, 'Earth'-like climates. Travelers of Rigelian or Klingon descent will find this world accommodating. Vulcans will find it tolerable, while humans describe it as hot.

WHAT TO WATCH OUT FOR Footwear is recommended when walking beaches at night when the sand wasps come out. They are small, burrowing creatures with atrophied wings (they cannot fly) and sharp stingers. Their sting is not as poisonous as that of an average Earth bee, but they are a nuisance. Remember to look where you walk at night, and always carry a laser-light.

FACTS TO TAKE INTO ACCOUNT Andor is crowded, and cities suffer from over-crowding. Resorts are outside major cities. Tourist excursions into the cities are convenient and available.

Andorians are friendly, though visitors should become familiar with their customs. For example, Andorians are hermaphroditic and can change sex according to the prefer-

FOCUS ON:

ANDOR: The more famous resorts, such as Teliv By The Sea and Cape Ghost are all located in areas of the most temperate and 'Earth'-like climates. If you are of Rigelian or Klingon descent, you will find this world quite accommodating. Vulcans will find it tolerable, while humans may describe it as hot. Andor is a world in the throes of over-population. Visiting it can be compared to visiting the Earth nation of Japan.

ANDROME-

ences of their partner. They do not distinguish differences between the sexes as many species do. Andorians are shrewd traders, and prefer to deal strictly in gold-pressed latinum. They will take UFP (United Federations of Planets) VISA, but they do not take UFP Express.

ANDROMEDA

The nearest galaxy to the Milky Way Galaxy, the Andromeda Galaxy, offers many interesting places to visit. Home to the Kelvans, a multi-tentacled, shape-shifting race, Andromeda also houses the ancient, unnamed race who built the long-lived androids inhabiting Mudd's Planet.

RECOMMENDATIONS FOR TRAVELERS This distant, uncharted galaxy is not recommended for those who cannot endure harsh, rigorous travel. The galaxy is three hundred Earth years from most points in our galaxy. Skilled pilots are necessary to navigate the galactic barrier. Immortals and long-term hibernators may pierce this final frontier. Generation ships are encouraged.

FACTS TO TAKE INTO ACCOUNT Kelvans are aggressive and war-like. They have developed a very advanced technology. The Federation Tour Bureau recommends bring-

FOCUS ON:

ANTOS IV: This is a temperate world, unpolluted, lush with plant growth, and has long, flat, white beaches and rolling turquoise seas. There are deserts and tundra, beautiful mountain ranges (for the mountain climbers among you) and natural, mostly harmless wildlife in abundance.

Attractions include: the Magician's Vortex — a place where the ocean and land meet in a constant whirlwind of water, and Starkiller's Alley — one of the galaxy's largest amusement parks. Sun worshippers and beachcombers will love the quiet beaches where many resorts offer hospitality of the most luxurious sort to nearly all species, including water-breathing and silicon-based life forms.

Hotels include the fabulous Luxor Mountain, the tallest structure on the planet. Guests can step from their room directly into a private cubicle that whisks them to the attraction of their choice at the touch of a finger pad.

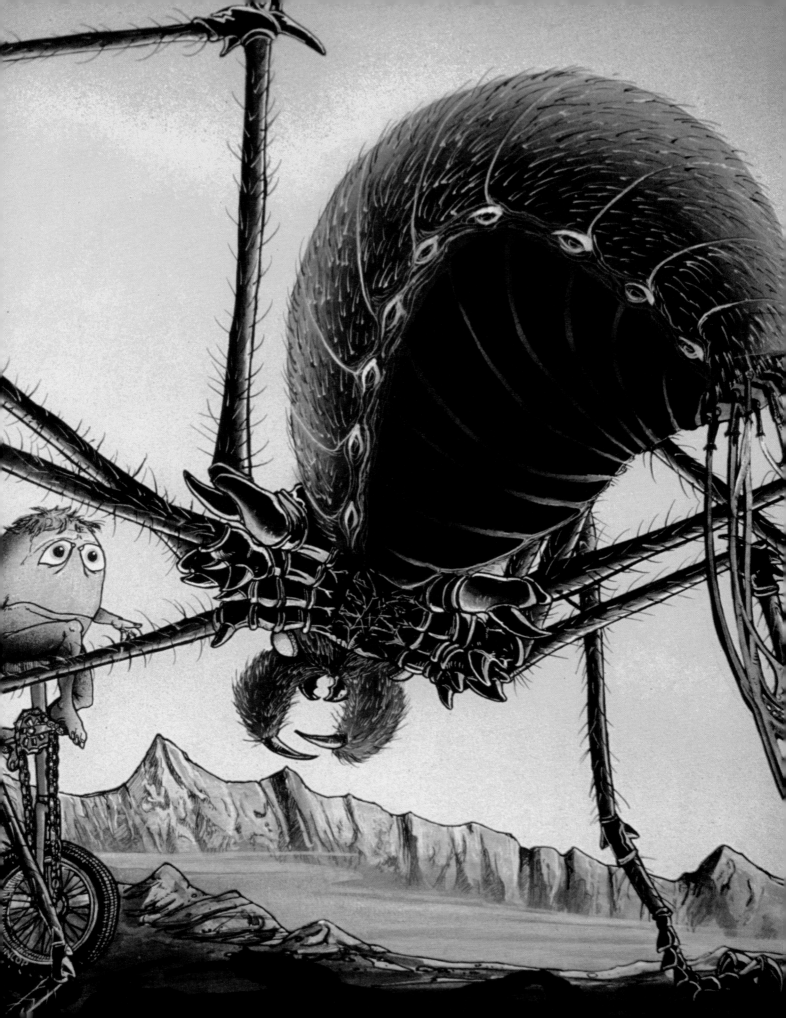

ing high-functioning cloaking devices for safety. If these cannot be acquired, ships must carry sufficient defense shields and weapons.

Radiation is increasing. Kelvans who visited the Milky Way in 2250 claim levels were low enough in 1950 to be harmless to most life forms. Levels may reach lethal levels in ten thousand years. Then proper shielding will offer protection from radiation poisoning.

The ancient creators of the androids on Mudd's Planet are believed to be extinct. Legend claims these magical beings left magnificent artifacts throughout the Andromeda Galaxy. These 'great wonders of the universe' are reputed to contain supernatural elements including doorways to other dimensions, and relics of such beauty and craftsmanship as to drive any mortal being mad.

Visitors to the Andromeda Galaxy must pack recording equipment. Inhabitants do not trade in UFP VISA or Mastercard; moneys must be in precious gems and metals. Kelvans love rare crystal (diamond, dilithium). They also trade in platinum, gold-pressed latinum and fragile statuettes of blown glass. They are attracted to delicate things because their awkward bulk does not allow them to create such objects themselves.

✪ ANGEL ONE

This world is a popular vacation spot for women. No male has chosen to visit Angel One. The society of Angel One makes men completely subservient to women.

The matriarchy is a reversal of the ancient, oppressive, male-dominated cultures of Earth or the Ferengi. Led by The Elected One, the businesslike women of Angel One appreciate the finer things in life. The planet offers many luxuries for space faring females. Servant men wait on them hand and foot, and cater to their every need.

Travelers don't stay long. Once the novelty wears off, visitors find it a profoundly unbalanced society. Female visitors from Federation worlds are often drawn by curiosity only to find the experience distasteful. A few like the system and apply for citizenship. Hotels are modest and do not welcome tourists.

✪ ANGOSIA

A class M world with beautiful cities, vast mountain ranges and tundra, forests, jungles, deserts and large oceans. Peace has been tenuous since the end of the Tarsian War. Conflict between civilians and genetically enhanced super soldiers makes tourism difficult. A few tourists visited this world unharmed. Prime Minister Nayrock of Angosia has little control over extremist factions. Veterans have used terrorist tactics to regain their rights in Angosian society.

Urban skirmishes still occur, making the world unpleasant for outside visitors. Angosians want tourism to increase. The intellectual, humanoid Angosians welcome foreign ideas. This planet will be a popular attraction soon.

RECOMMENDATIONS FOR TRAVELERS Lunar V, a satellite of Angosia, holds the penal colony imprisoning super soldiers from the Tarsian War. Plans exist to open the now vacant jail as a historical attraction complete with gift shop, cafeteria and holo projections. Opening date has not been set.

FACTS TO TAKE INTO ACCOUNT Angosians are intellectuals prizing rare books and artifacts of other civilizations. Rare books containing stories, especially poetry, bring a high price on the open market. You could pay for your trip with one rare book. Angosians do not take credit cards and are not yet a member of the Federation. That could change soon.

ANTEDE III

Antedians live in the vast, blue seas of this water world. They welcome other water-breathers, but discourage non-water-breathers from visiting. A few ships and floating way stations exist for official visitors. Antedians abhor space flight and travel only in a catatonic state. The fragile beings do not like to disrupt their underwater life.

RECOMMENDATIONS FOR TRAVELERS A new member of the United Federation of Planets, Antedians are curious about other water-breathing races. They welcome tourism and are very friendly within their own environment. Their amazing underwater cities offer towering crystal spires and shell-lined waterways on the sea floor. Their cities are safe from predators that inhabit other underwater villages, such as sharks and stinger-fish. Antede's seas are tropical except at the poles, which are avoided by most life forms. Water-breathers from colder, deep sea environments may find the warm Antede waters unpleasant. Cooling protective suits are available. Tours the ruins of this world's ancient, drowned city are reported to be fascinating. Picture brochures are available from the Federation Tourist Bureau upon request.

FACTS TO TAKE INTO ACCOUNT   Antedes are vegetarians. No meat is served on this world. The peaceful natives maintain a safe environment for visitors. There is a clothing-optional law as in many water-breathing societies because unnecessary accessories hamper underwater movement. Nudity is common.

Off-world trade is conducted with Federation credits, but local merchants prefer cash, notes bearing values defined by pearls and precious shells. A special charge is added to purchases made with Federation credits. UFP VISA is now accepted. It is hoped that, in the future, other credit cards will also be accepted.

ANTICA

This world of the Beta Renner System is at war with its neighbor, Selay. This is not a recommended vacation spot due to frequent violence. Anticans do not like outsiders, especially war correspondents. Antica is a forested world. Anticans are wolf-like humanoids.

They are pack oriented and territorial. They currently possess interplanetary but not interstellar space flight. Anticans are friendly but aggressive to outsiders, and not yet a member of the United Federation of Planets. Their neighbor, Selay, is the home of a reptilian species. The complex dispute between Antica and Selay shows no signs of ending.

RECOMMENDATIONS FOR TRAVELERS This world is at war. When approaching, you must immediately broadcast an S.O.S. including your identity and your peaceful intentions. Anticans will not shoot alien spacecraft if they are not from Selay. Antica has cold winters and cool summers due to the heavy forests. The world also has mountains and salt seas, and poles covered in ice. There are many points of special interest, including Pyramid Glacier. The Great Goldwood Forest contains millennium old trees with trunks nearly a quarter of a mile in diameter. The Ruins of Doggus surround an ancient temple that resembles those left by the legendary Preservers.

FACTS TO TAKE INTO ACCOUNT Anticans are carnivorous. They are very protective of their young. Approaching a young Antican without the full prior approval of the parents can elicit an immediate attack. Local customs include singing similar to a prayer

FOCUS ON:

ARGELIUS II: The world where adult entertainment reigns supreme; not intended for family outings. The Argelian Humanoid Erotic Dance Troupe is praised throughout the galaxy. Their shows appeal to all genders of any sexual orientation, and are not to be missed. Shopping on Argelius is a treat. Here, you can find gifts for those 'hard to shop for' family members or friends on your list. This is a shopper's paradise.

Resorts offer large, spacious rooms with the utmost privacy (or not, depending on what you request). Each room has its own private pool and Jacuzzi. Robot bartenders and chefs will see to your every culinary need. You will have access to elaborate exercise rooms and virtual reality fantasy rooms. The resorts also allow gambling.

Argelius' adult amusement parks are not to be missed. X-rated brochures with detailed descriptions of these parks are available on request from the Federation Tourist Bureau.

Favored hotels include the Oral Combination and the Howard Johnson's Miraculous Positions.

or benediction before every meal and at night when the moons rise. Antican singing voices are among the most beautiful in the galaxy, second only to the Lorelei. The Antican greeting consists of a pat on the head instead of a handshake, but they will not be offended if you hold your hand (or paw) out by mistake.

Anticans trade in local money consisting of polished bone inlaid with gold and silver. They do not take Federation currency or credit cards. Gold press latinum impresses Anticans. They are eager to buy alien weapons, but Federation policy prohibits selling guns to non-Federation worlds. Strict penalties include high fines and six months at a Van Gelder mind-wipe clinic for the 'conscientiously-challenged.'

⊚ antos IV

Natives of this peaceful, class M world are shapechangers. It was home for a time for the famous Garth of Izar. The preserved house where Garth lived remains. It is the building in which he learned the art of shape-changing from the natives. It is also where he went mad, turned his powers against them and fled the planet in an attempt to take over the known universe.

RECOMMENDATIONS FOR TRAVELERS A temperate, beautiful world free of pollution and filled with lush plant growth. It offers long, flat, white beaches, rolling turquoise seas, deserts, tundra, beautiful mountain ranges and natural, mostly harmless wildlife in abundance. Insects are a problem, but light force shields keep them away from human inhabited areas.

Besides the places where Garth lived, there are many other attractions. The Magician's Vortex is a place where ocean and land meet in a constant whirlwind of water. Starkiller's Alley is one of the galaxy's largest amusement parks. Sun worshippers and beachcombers will love the quiet beaches, with their many luxurious resorts that cater to nearly all species, including water-breathing and silicon-based life forms.

FACTS TO TAKE INTO ACCOUNT Antosians are nearly indistinguishable from Earth humans. They are artisans and priests, fascinated by the infinite possibilities of the mind. Vulcans will be interested in Antosian mind-healing techniques. Their shape-changing talent requires years of great discipline. They are proud of this technique, and offer classes to newcomers. Unfortunately these classes only tease as you will learn little unless you devote yourself to the mental arts for many years. Antosians work as a race to improve their telepathic talents with each generation. They study Vulcan mind-meld techniques, and welcome Vulcan visitors with great enthusiasm. Trade between Antos and Vulcan is good. Friendship is good for both races, and there have been many interracial Vulcan/Antosian marriages in recent years.

Antosians are members of the United Federation of Planets, and take all Federation currency and credit cards. Gambling is illegal. Crime is almost non-existent. As on Antede, clothing is optional. Antosians believe in the beauty of the natural body. They do not exploit nudity or favor wanton sex. This is not an adults-only world. Parents of young children can rest assured their young will be safe and welcome. The G-rated shape-changing shows and plays Antosians put on are not to be missed. These inexpensive, elaborate live shows are everywhere, at resorts and small towns.

ARDANA

This class M world is home to one of the most beautiful cities in the known galaxy, the sky-city Stratos. The city is constructed with some of the most advanced technology available in the Federation. It floats on huge anti-gravity struts. On a clear day, the view from Stratos is incredible. When the clouds part, it is like looking into another dimension. Ardana is green and verdant, striped with rivers and canals. Most Ardanans do not live on the surface, but in the city of Stratos, or below the surface in make-shift towns that service the mines that make Ardana one of the Federation's richest worlds.

RECOMMENDATIONS FOR TRAVELERS Camping and hiking the rich, preserved wildernesses of Ardana is an experience no outdoors-person will ever forget. Wildlife is abundant and varied. Tuft-eared miniphants and squirrel-cats are practically domesticated and will eat from your hand. The trails lead to never-ending panoramas of beauty. On this 'protected' world, hunting is illegal. Ardanans are strict vegetarians. The most popular tourist attraction is the city Stratos, filled with museums and cultural centers. This fantastic city offers a delightful array of attractions. The Ardanans value science and art, so whatever your interest, there will be a museum, class or shop for you.

FACTS TO TAKE INTO ACCOUNT Ardanans love visitors. They are friendly and chatty with almost no crime. Prime Minister Droxine Plasus-the-third follows in her mother's and grandmother's footsteps by assuring all beings are treated with respect and equality. They learned tolerance and fairness from their recent past, when zenite gas temporarily rendered miners brain-damaged. The old Stratos government thought it an evolutionary mishap and treated the troglodyte miners as inferiors with few rights. They became slaves to the intellectualized people of Stratos.

When off-worlders discovered zenite gas had effected the miners, and was reversible, the Stratos government changed the laws. Troglodyte miners were given full rights of citizenship. Mining chores were later shared by all citizens. At some point, every Ardanan gains experience in the mines. The Ardanans trade in zenite and take all Federation currency and credit cards. They are currently hard at work building a second, large sky city. Ionos is planned to be ten times the size of Stratos.

ARGELIUS II

This class M world is a pleasure planet. Tourism is the number one source of income. The world is strictly for adults, although there is a nursery. Adult entertainment of all varieties can be found. There has been virtually no crime for centuries, though there are strict laws to keep visitors safe. The only reported criminal case in this century involved an alien entity. The entity subsisted on fear and death, and murdered women to feed. The entity was caught and destroyed. Argelians insist this incident was not their fault and that they dealt with it quickly and efficiently. The planet is ranked the safest world in the known galaxy.

RECOMMENDATIONS FOR TRAVELERS The Argelian Humanoid Erotic Dance Troupe is praised throughout the galaxy. Their shows appeal to all genders of any sexual orientation. Shopping is a treat on Argelius. Stores offer gifts for those 'hard to shop for' family members or friends on your list. Many erotica stores offer art, toys, alien artifacts, literature, soaps, scents and lotions. Argelians also sell products that are not of a sexual nature. They love games, jewelry, exotic clothing, furniture and knickknacks. This is a shopper's paradise with reasonable prices. Their resorts offer large, spacious rooms with complete privacy—or not, depending on your request. Each room has its own private pool and Jacuzzi. Robot bartenders and chefs fill every culinary need. Elaborate exercise and virtual reality fantasy facilities are available. The resorts allow gambling. Argelius' adult amusement parks are not to be missed. X-rated brochures are available on request from the Federation Tourist Bureau with detailed descriptions of these parks.

FACTS TO TAKE INTO ACCOUNT Argelians pride themselves on abundant sexual freedom. They are not monogamous and most are bisexual. Public sex is not illegal, but uncommon. They believe in pleasure of all kinds. The only fetishes they do not permit are rape, victimization of any life form and pedophilia. There is no disease, and no hazards to tourists.

All tourists must pass through customs. Mandatory inoculations prevent outsiders from bringing disease into the purified communities. Young Argelians are raised in boarding schools away from the influences of the pleasure world. When they mature, they may choose to remain on Argelius or go off-world to pursue independent careers. Argelians treat all sexes and species with respect and equality, and expect the same in return. They love the diversity of species that visits their world, and work hard to accommodate even the non-humanoid of the galaxy. Argelians use advanced climatology to keep their planet at moderate temperatures year round. They take all Federation currency and credit cards.

FOCUS ON:

ARDANA: The sky city, Stratos, remains the hub of activity. The city hangs suspended more than a mile above the ground. Every room in the fabulous Sunlight Garden Hotel has a bay window looking offering panoramic views of the planet below.

Shuttles are available for trips to the surface. The vast river network has airboats for rent or for tours that take visitors skimming over the surface of these winding, serpentine watery thoroughfares.

⊚ARGUS X

Argus X, a class M planet, is barren of all animal life. It is mostly rock with little water. The world is prone to high, keening winds and was once the home of a gaseous cloud life form that drains blood from victims to feed. It is not known if Argus X was its natural home. The creature was destroyed by a Federation starship. If others exist on Argus X, they have not been found.

RECOMMENDATIONS FOR TRAVELERS This world is not industrialized, and has no provisions for human or non-human life forms. High winds make it uncomfortable for camping, hiking or rock climbing. All water must be imported. The Federation Tourist Bureau does not recommend this world as a vacation spot. This may change in the future as mining rights are being investigated. This world is not 'protected'; if miners move in, cities may follow. Argus is reputed to have natural underground grottoes with harvestable water. The grottoes might make interesting tourist attractions away from the harsh winds. These underground pools may be naturally heated. Exploration of this world has been cursory; facts are sparse. For now, stay away.

⊚ARRET

Arretians moved underground when the surface of their world became unlivable due to wars. The surface is still dangerous. There are miles of tunnels leading to subterranean chambers. Three survivors were found 75 years ago in circular receptacles that held the essence of their minds and souls. They tried, with the help of a passing starship, to build inhabitable robot bodies, but the ordeal was too difficult. They dissipated before the project could be completed. The spheres in which the minds were kept are a major tourist attraction on Arret.

RECOMMENDATIONS FOR TRAVELERS You must plan ahead to visit Arret as there is a waiting list. The underground chambers accommodate only several hundred people at a time. Orbiting hotels offer conveniences to travelers. Transporters take people below for the tour. The temperature in the caves is cool, and beings sensitive to cold should dress accordingly.

FACTS TO TAKE INTO ACCOUNT Arretians evolved to a form that needed no physical body, and were telepaths able to create and destroy with a thought. Their talents were too powerful for them to control, even with their great intellects, and they soon destroyed themselves. This ancient people's memory is preserved in the chambers. All that is left is contained in the underground chambers. The tours are arranged by the Federation Tourist Bureau, and all moneys collected go to the upkeep of this 'natural' museum. The orbiting hotels are privately owned and run by Orion/Tellarite co-ops.

 BAJOR

This beautiful world on the edge of the Alpha Quadrant has only recently been opened to the Federation. Until two years ago it carried a traveler warning, "visit at your own risk," due to civil war against the Cardassians occupiers.

After 60 years extracting mineral wealth from the planet, the Cardassians withdrew, claiming they chose to grant Bajor its independence. Actually Bajor was an independent, self-sustaining world before the Cardassians invaded.

The Bajoran system includes several planets. Bajor is the largest and most populous. Bajor has five moons and provides access to the only known "stable" wormhole, connecting the Alpha Quadrant with the Gamma Quadrant. Bajor Eight hosts a lower moon called Andros Two-B.

Bajor's fifth moon is Jeraddo. It is the subject of Bajor's first large-scale energy transfer from the tapping of its molten core in quadrant fifteen delta. The habitable moon was evacuated and its 50 inhabitants resettled, but not without resistance.

IMPORTANT ATTRACTIONS Kai Taluno, the 22nd century Bajoran leader, claims to have had a vision in which the heavens opened and nearly swallowed his ship. This was the first evidence of the Wormhole.

The Bajoran wormhole, a charged plasma field in space, is located in the Denorios Asteroid Belt. At least five of the Tears of the Prophets were found here.

The Celestial Temple is the legendary home of the Prophets, the gods of the Bajorans. Nine orbs called Tears of the Prophets apparently originated in the Temple. The Celestial Temple is the Wormhole. Bajoran religious devotees who study the Tears of the Prophets are called Monks.

The Bajoran wormhole is artificial, the only stable wormhole ever constructed. It is a gateway to the Gamma Quadrant ordinarily 70 thousand light-years away. The Gamma Quadrant remains unexplored although visitors from the quadrant visit our quadrant on a regular basis. The Federation has no treaty with any planet in the Gamma Quadrant and exploration has only recently begun.

The former mining station now known as Deep Space Nine orbits Bajor, at the gateway to the wormhole. Built eighteen years before the Federation arrived, this station is now maintained jointly by the Federation and the Bajorans. Capable of holding 7,000 people, its most prominent feature is the Promenade, a bazaar of the bizarre. Gambling is offered in holosuites in "Quark's Place." Bajoran merchants hawk their varied wares.

Three hundred people live on the station that exists to monitor the wormhole. Five or six ships dock each week. The station is divided into 19 sections, with a Habitat Ring containing guest quarters located in corridor H-12-A. It is equipped with shields and constructed from the Cardassian metal, Duranium.

THE FUTURE AND THE PAST Bajor has limited space flight using impulse drives, but no warp drive. Cardassia annexed Bajor. Since liberation from the Cardassians, Bajor has become dependent on the tourist trade. It is now aligned with the Federation and part of the galactic marketplace.

Some of the most interesting sights on Bajor are tourist centers built to welcome visitors to the scenic wonders of this old world and its rich cultural heritage. Bajor offers striking architecture with rounded domes; spherical shapes mark the landscape. The ancients of Bajor were gifted architects and engineers when life on Earth was just entering the Stone Age.

All cities participate in the planet's large annual celebration, the Gratitude Festival. The celebration now commemorates independence, although in times past it celebrated the bounty granted by the Prophets, the legendary figures of Bajor's religion.

Bajor is a very spiritual society. The leader is known as the Kai. The Kai Opaka told Federation representative Commander Ben Sisko that he had been chosen by the Prophets as the "Emissary." This led to contact between the Federation and the religious of Bajor.

Vedeks are subordinate to the Kai. There are 112 Vedeks forming a governing body called the Vedek Assembly.

Bajorans believe strange objects known as "orbs" grant them visions of the future. The Orbs, also known as the Tears of the Prophets, are glowing devices housed in jeweled cases. They can send someone out of 'linear time' and make

FOCUS ON:

BENZAR: This world is not hospitable to offworlders because of an atmosphere most humanoids would regard as thin. Pleasure domes have been constructed for visitors.

The vast pale green sands of the Benzite deserts are quite beautiful. Special breathing equipment is required unless you are satisfied with traveling inside an enclosed sand crawler.

Holiday Inn was the first terrestrial establishment to build a resort here. They were particularly attracted to the generous and gracious nature of the Benzites. Benzites make such perfect hotel employees that some have been transferred offworld to run other Holiday Inns and to train hotel managers in new methods of being gracious and helpful.

all memories part of the present. Nine of the Orbs appeared in the skies of Bajor over the past ten thousand years. The Cardassians took eight.

The Prophets from the Celestial Temple sent the orbs to instruct Bajorans. At least five of the orbs were found in the Denorios Belt.

FACTS TO TAKE INTO ACCOUNT The Bajoran spiritual lifeforce, or soul, is known as the Pagh. Bajorans believe the Kai can feel a Pagh by holding the subject's ear. The Pagh can be replenished by the Prophets.

The Kai lives in seclusion and rarely sees anyone. The recent loss of the Kai Opaka created political turmoil in the new Bajoran Provisional government. The matter has not been completely resolved.

Vedek Bareil is a soft-spoken man in his '30s. When he was a child, he vowed to rid his society of the archaic ritual of ear clasping. He is expected to become the next Kai.

Another high-ranking Bajoran religious official is Vedek Winn, a cleric in the Bajoran orthodox order. She is a tough woman in her 60's who wants to be Kai. She often resorts to thinly veiled threats. Her followers blew up the school on Deep Space Nine during a religious dispute with the teacher. Another of her followers attempted to assassinate Vedek Bareil. Vedek Winn was never officially tied to the incident although she witnessed it.

Members of the Bajoran Provisional Government with voting privileges are called Ministers. The Minister of State of Bajor is Kaval. An Arbiter is a Bajoran legal judge who can even preside over extradition hearings. Bajor has penitentiaries, including the Kran Tobal Prison.

RECOMMENDATIONS FOR TRAVELERS Bajor offers the traveler rich scenic wonders, the most notable being the spectacular Fire Caverns in the little populated Kendar region. Special tours show of the volcanic rivers of fire are a highlight. The river of molten rock provides the only illumination in a cavern more than two hundred feet tall, with walls glistening with rock formations polished by heat.

The North Eastern District of the planet is home to the Ilvian Medical complex. Lasuma contains a grain-processing center.

There is also a Transit Aid Center on Bajor used specifically by visitors for information and assistance. Ask for Zayra.

The Archival of Records holds the massive Bajoran library. It was preserved from destruction by the Cardassians by being hidden in remote locations scattered across the globe. It took many months to retrieve the records and restore them to a single location, saving Bajor's rich heritage and history.

The performing arts center in the capital city of Bajor is still under construction. The world's minstrels have become wanderers, performing wherever they find welcome. They bring joy to the daily life of a proud people as they fight to regain their culture. Bajoran musical compositions are known as Serenas and run the gamut from dark and soulful to bright and exuberant.

THE PEOPLE OF BAJOR The Bajoran people need to be united by stories such as that of the Dal'Rok. The legendary Dal'Rok threatens a Bajoran tribe during each harvest time. It is a terrible cloud creature that creates wind and lightning. It lives in the Bajoran woods descending for five nights every year at the end of the harvest.

Only the Sirah can defeat it by telling a loud ritual tale. The Sirah wears a bright orange robe as part of his ceremonial ritual. The Dal'Rok doesn't register on sensors because it is really the fear of the villagers in physical form. A fragment of the Tear of the Prophet orb creates the Dal'Rok.

A tessipate is the unit of measurement of land on Bajor.

There is an old saying on Bajor: "The land and the people are one." There is a land dispute involving the Glyrhond River, the border between the Paqu and the Navot clans. The Paqu avoid contact with outsiders, and a dispute occurred when the Cardassians altered the flow of the river. This affected the terms of the 90 year old Paqu/Navot treaty. The treaty stated, "The border separating the Paqu and the Navot shall forever be the river Glyrhond."

The Paqu clan, rivals of the Navot clan, is led by a 15 year-old girl, Tetrarch Varis Sul. Her parents were killed by the Cardassians. Her father was a great and strong leader, feared by the Navot, but not afraid to compromise. The feud ended when land was exchanged for free trade access to both sides of the river.

Gallitepp is the site of a former Cardassian forced labor camp. Survivors of a mining accident in the camp contracted Kalla-Nohra syndrome. Kalla-Nohra is chronic and requires medication, but it is not contagious and can not be contracted by off-worlders. Survivors of Gallitepp are a living symbol of Bajoran strength and courage. They are embraced by their countrymen.

Gallitepp, under the command of Gul Darhe'el, the Butcher Of Gallitepp, was the site of the worst atrocities committed by the Cardassians. It was liberated by the Bajoran resistance in the final days of the Cardassian occupation.

PLANT AND ANIMAL LIFE Bajoran wildlife includes the Kandipper, a small aquatic animal. It is mentioned in many Bajoran proverbs, such as in the phrase: "like spearing kandippers in a bottle." Rastipods are carnivorous animals, about three meters long and one meter tall at the shoulder.

Kellipates are Bajoran flowers that need sunlight to flourish. They are particularly gorgeous in the winter months and thrive in icy climes, drawing life from nutrients in frozen water. They often grow through cracks in the ice.

Bajorans are more concerned with rebuilding their society than tourism. Visitors are welcome but the only hotel is Deep Space Nine. It is capable of housing several thousand visitors at a time.

BAJOR

THE BAJORAN WORMHOLE The new Gamma Quadrant frontier is ripe for pleasure travel. Some hardy souls venture to Bajor, a forbidding place in the grip of reconstruction and civil turmoil after years of Cardassian occupation.

The Bajoran Wormhole is still the only stable sub-space shortcut. Other wormholes are notoriously unstable, appearing and disappearing with amazing speed. The Barzan Wormhole is the most notorious recent example. Some appear stable for a time, but this is on one end; the other end might shift light-years every time the wormhole opens. Complete wormhole collapse is particularly hazardous.

One greedy Ferengi failed to take this into account and wound up stranded in the Delta Quadrant, seventy years from known space. The mishap has become the basis for many Ferengi jokes of the past several years.

A wormhole could even reach from one galaxy to another, but none such have been reported. Anyone foolhardy enough to risk such a trip has yet to return to tell of their experiences.

INSIDE THE WORMHOLE The stable Bajoran Wormhole was unknown until after the Cardassian withdrawal from Bajor. The Wormhole may be an artifact of an unknown alien race. This belief is the basis for many mystical aspects of Bajoran religion.

Rumors insist the current Starfleet representative, Commander Benjamin Sisko of the Deep Space Nine station, encountered these beings. This has never

FOCUS ON:

BETA III: This is a green, temperate world with vast oceans and lush continents. A member in good standing with the Federation, this world offers four star accommodations including the most modern floating hotels.

The hotels travel across the bi-lateral ocean, stopping at various ports of call where one can disembark for sightseeing and exploring. The hotel can be rejoined any time en route thanks to their modern intercity transportation grid of hovercraft. Recommended hotels include the Continental Drift, Beta III At Sea and the Ariel. All Federation currencies accepted at the Exchange Mart.

It is advisable to make reservations at least six months in advance, particularly for the spring season when the annual Festival is celebrated in the city of Reger. Local ordinances forbid celebration of the Red Hour, although some have revived the free-for-all as long as no one fights back.

been officially confirmed. Riding through the wormhole offers an amazing visual journey more fantastic than any chemical induced fantasy.

Colors, lights and vibrating strands of subspace matter all cascade past the spacecraft. No one, not even a Ferengi, has officially arranged for a vessel to provide round trips through the Wormhole for sightseers. It is easy to obtain passage to the Gamma Quadrant on one craft, and transfer to a returning spacecraft for the trip home.

One caution: there's not much to do in the Gamma Quadrant. It is wise to book your return voyage with this in mind. Arrangements can be made by contacting the Quark association on Deep Space Nine. Be certain to double-check all scheduling promises with the official Starfleet authorities. Complaints of unscheduled week-long sojourns by tourists forced to live off replicator gruel have been reported.

The Federation has no treaties with worlds in the Gamma Quadrant. Some worlds are unfriendly to visitors. [See THE GAMMA QUADRANT listing.]

BARZAN II

This planet is in the double-star system near the notorious Barzan Wormhole. The wormhole appeared stable but was not, and the Barzans may have been fully aware of this.

A wormhole is a transdimensional gateway to another point in the galaxy. The Barzan wormhole opened every 233 minutes due to radiation in the accretion disk. Mesons and leptons ultimately caused instability. The wormhole offered a shortcut to the Gamma Quadrant. This would have opened commerce and exploration. Unfortunately, the wormhole abruptly changed the location of its exit point, making it valueless and unreliable.

The Barzans sold exclusive rights to the Ferengi. Two Ferengi representatives were later trapped in the Gamma Quadrant when the wormhole changed its exit point.

Barzan is poor world. It used the Ferengi money to begin developing resources previously unreachable below ground. The planet's minuscule gross national product prevented it from obtaining credit in the intergalactic marketplace.

Since the notorious Barzan wormhole deal was made, the planetary economy has boomed. Delightful resorts have appeared in equatorial regions.

The motto is: "Avoid the crowds at Risa—see the Barzan double sunset."

BENZAR

Benzites are obsessed with impressing people. The bluish-gray skinned, hairless humanoids must wear a special device to breathe in class-M atmospheres, such as on most starships. Their own atmosphere is low in hydrogen.

BENZAR

Benzar is not hospitable to most humanoids because of its thin atmosphere. Pleasure domes have been constructed for visitors, but many are put off by having to wear special breathing equipment to cross the beautiful pale green deserts. Some choose to travel inside an enclosed sand crawler.

Holiday Inn, the first Terrestrial company to build a resort, was attracted by the generous, gracious nature of the Benzites. Benzites made such perfect hotel employees that some have been transferred offworld to run other Holiday Inns and train managers.

BERSALLIS III

There is a Federation outpost on this beautiful yet dangerous world. The rocky planet has mountain ranges thousands of feet high which sweep down into broad bowls of massive deserts.

It would be possible to terraform the planet if the strange atmosphere could be conquered. Firestorms flare out of control every Fall. They burn from a low of two thousand degrees to a high end several times that. They can be so intense and furious that even force fields cannot block them.

The Federation outpost was evacuated when a storm of unprecedented magnitude overwhelmed the Thermal Deflector Units. The evacuation was achieved only at a loss of several crewmen from the Enterprise. The crewman manned the Deflector Units while the colonists evacuated. When the units were overwhelmed by the fury of the storm, the away team was consumed.

This world is open to authorized Federation personnel with scientific visas and prior approval from Starfleet. Explorers are not allowed to establish permanent ground sites but must maintain a vessel in constant stationary orbit.

Bersallis III is unsuitable for terraforming or colonizing. Tourist visas are not granted to visit this world. Anyone visiting the world illegally and requiring rescue will be billed for the full cost of extraction and transport and face severe criminal penalties.

BETA III

A Class M planet in Star System 6-11 first visited by the USS Archon in the 22nd century. Survivors of the Archon were absorbed by the native culture. Until the 23rd century, a primitive society, comparable to mid-20th century Earth ran the planet.

The people known as "The Body" was ruled by a super computer named Landru. The computer preserved the personality of a previous living ruler. Rather than governing wisely, the machine caused cultural stagnation.

The populace found living as "The Body" stressful. One night each year Landru released them to run amok during the night of The Festival, raping and pillaging to release tension. At the end of the night, Landru resumed control and The Body continued as before.

Landru was located behind a wall in the Hall of Audiences. His servants were called Lawgivers and carried a staff with which to punish or kill dissenters. Survivors of the Archon preached insurrection until they were absorbed into The Body.

Captain James T. Kirk and a landing party from the Enterprise were named "Archons" by the Betans. They were asked to help against the tyranny of Landru. James Kirk revealed Landru was a computer and destroyed the machine's influence over the people.

FACTS TO TAKE INTO ACCOUNT Betans resumed their normal development. Eighty years have passed and a generation has grown up remembering Landru only as an image on a videologue and a fable. Children often shout: "watch out or Landru will get you!"

Motion pictures present the return of Landru as a threat the hero must overcome. One popular videologue mini-series chronicles the people of Beta III rising up to defeat a modern successor to the super computer. There is even a series of adventure novels featuring the menace of Landru.

A small splinter group of "Neo-Landrus" believe their world was better under such domination because crime and poverty didn't exist. They claim that the deaths inflicted by the Lawgivers was exaggerated and the Red Hour is a myth. This group has been outlawed and their activities are closely monitored.

THE WORLD TODAY Super computers are illegal on Beta III. Instead such tasks are delegated to a series of interconnected computers, none of which could disrupt the society.

The green, temperate world possesses vast oceans and lush continents. Landru preserved the ecosystem and scanned and logged all mineral deposits. After the fall of Landru, it was easy to mine the minerals and set up interplanetary trading concerns. They have rapidly rebuilt the stagnant society into an exciting world.

This Federation member offers four star accommodations including modern floating hotels that travel across the bi-lateral ocean. They stop at varied ports of call to allow guests to disembark for sightseeing and exploration. The hotel can be rejoined at any point en route thanks to a grid of hovercraft. Reservations must be made at least six months in advance, particularly for the spring season when the annual Festival is celebrated in the city of Reger. Most local ordinances forbid celebration of the Red Hour.

All forms of Federation currency and barter are gratefully accepted.

 **BETAZED**

Betazed is home to many scenic wonders. Foremost of these is the Janarian Falls, spectacular cascades that have inspired lovers for countless centuries. Betazed is a true gar-

BETAZED

den spot, with a vast, and sometimes bewildering, array of gorgeous plant life. The warm hospitality of humanoid natives, the telepathic Betazoids, welcomes visitors to one of the most enjoyable worlds in the Federation.

Some visitors are concerned by the telepathy of the Betazoids. This should not to be a worry. Betazoids limit use of their empathic powers so as not to pry into the thoughts of others. Some species, such as the Ferengi and Dropterians, are immune to this telepathy.

Natural empathy makes it almost impossible for Betazoids not to discern your general emotional state. Most Betazoids use this power graciously towards visitors, and are very attentive to guests.

Betazoid telepathy is a highly advanced form of empathy. Direct mind-to-mind communication is possible only between full or half-Betazoids.

Theoretically telepathy between Betazoids and Vulcans should be possible, but the two races choose not to communicate in this fashion. That Betazoids are highly emotional and Vulcans are purely logical may have something to do with this. Telepathic abilities develop with the onset of puberty, at about the same age as in humans. Humans and Betazoids can have children together. Half-Betazoids usually have advanced empathic abilities but are limited telepathically.

In rare instances a Betazoid is born with functional powers. These individuals, if they survive, become the most powerful telepaths, but suffer unstable personalities. Their socializing skills are devastated by their premature telepathic development. At present there are no such Betazoids living on the planet.

FACTS TO TAKE INTO ACCOUNT Betazoid culture has many formalized rituals. Even an informal Betazoid dinner is accompanied by the ringing of chimes to express gratitude for the food. Some find this charming practice annoying.

A completely formal, traditional Betazoid meal can take up to four hours because of ritualized divisions by spiritual significance— in many ways the opposite of Earth's ancient tea ceremonies, which stressed simplicity. These meals are available at certain establishments by prior reservation.

Betazoid cuisine is flavorful.

The Betazoid marriage ceremony, or joining, involves complete nudity of all participants. This sometimes causes difficulties when a Betazoid marries a mate from another humanoid race. Betazoids value friendship to a high degree. To be called "Imzadi" by a Betazoid is to have become a beloved part of their life forever.

Betazed trades with other worlds and offers a full array of four star hotels such as the Hilton Hightower. Fifty restaurants in the capitol city of Burrar specialize in the cuisine of other worlds, although there are no Klingon restaurants on Betazed.

◎ *BONESTELL RECREATION FACILITY*

This facility is located at Starbase Earhart and once had an unsavory reputation as a gambling den and intergalactic crossroads where the worst sort of galactic riffraff would gather. But that was in times past.

Today this glittering jewel in the firmament of space travel is a drop-ship point for recent graduates of Starfleet. Recent cadets meet other graduates and new crew mates to discuss their future.

Formerly open to anyone, the Bonestell Recreation Facility is now open only to Starfleet personnel and their families. Other visas are granted on a limited, and usually friends-of-the-family basis.

Starships stop at Starbase Earhart on a regular basis for routine maintenance and R&R.

◎ *BRE'EL IV*

This planet was recently threatened by catastrophe when the orbit of its single moon began to decay. Geologic disturbances would have torn Bre'el Four apart. A Federation starship tried to halt the catastrophe to no avail.

The destruction was averted by a member of the Q Continuum, a strange group of super-powerful, non-humanoid beings from an unknown region of space. They sometimes adopt humanoid form to interact with Federation species.

The moon was placed in a more stable orbit. Such a catastrophe can not threaten the world again for at least another million years.

A NEW RELIGION The near destruction of the world and impossibility of evacuation led to a doom watch that, when averted, spawned a new religion. Some Bre'els now worship the Q. Unlike other religions whose gods lived centuries before and whose deeds are recorded only in ancient tomes, this is the most widely recorded event in the history of the planet.

Dispute arises over the Q. Is there only one Q or many, and if there are many is there then an entire pantheon of gods? Since the Q use no identifying signatures, the worshipers on Bre'el Four have attached their own designations drawn

---

FOCUS ON:

 BETAZED: Betazed has a great deal of commerce with other worlds and offers a full array of four star hotels such as the Hilton Hightower, The Tellarite Tower and the Orion Comfort Zone. Fifty restaurants in the capitol city of Burrar specialize in the cuisine of other worlds, although there are no Klingon restaurants on Betazed.

BRE'EL IV

from their world's history. Although a small religion, their membership is intensely loyal and a chapel can be found in nearly all major cities.

Bre'el Four is as distant from its sun as Earth is from Sol. Climates and land masses are similar, although the land of Bre'el Four clusters around the equator.

The far north and south are oceans because ice caps shattered when the moon approached the planet. Federation technology has kept the ice from drifting and choking the inlets of continental masses. Geological shifts have been stabilized.

Visitors often fly over the northern sea of ice floes. Scientists probe the shattered ice for archeological secrets that may have surfaced. There is much to behold on this world brought back from the brink of destruction.

[See FORBIDDEN ZONES]

Bynaeus is in the Beta Magellan System. Bynars are paired for life and coexist as part of a worldwide organic computer.

FOCUS ON:

BYNAEUS: Bynaeus is, to some, their worst nightmare. While people on other worlds have complained that everything is being built up and paved over, on Bynaeus everything really has been built up and paved over. The Bynars believe that they have no need for grass, trees and flowers but love metal and concrete.

They enjoy modern air recirculating plants so that the atmosphere is cleaner than worlds far less industrialized than Bynaeus. It's a great place to visit if you like metal and concrete as far as the eye can see— and people who all look "similar" (never say out loud on Bynaeus that all the people look alike—it vexes them).

Hotels exist but they are indistinguishable from one another and have no names, just numbers. Tourists have become lost and wandered around, unable to find the proper number where they were staying. To Bynars, forgetting a number is unthinkable.

These humanoid beings don't function like people on other worlds but act as extensions of the super computer that runs their world. Some compare them to inhabitants of Beta III when it was under Landru 80 years ago. Others suggest that their close contact with the worldwide computer net is disturbingly reminiscent of the Borg.

The Bynars insist they are a benevolent society. This view suffered when four Bynars engineered the theft of the Enterprise-D. They wanted to use the starship's computer to reboot their own when it suffered a shutdown.

The Bynars first discussed asking the Federation for help but decided not to risk being refused. Instead the four Bynars volunteered to take responsibility and surrender to Starfleet for prosecution when their mission was accomplished.

This willingness to accept punishment for their crime demonstrates the desperation of their act. They insist this proves their good intentions.

FACTS TO TAKE INTO ACCOUNT Visiting Bynaeus is a strange experience. Bynars seem like clones when they are not. They try to look and act alike and take great pride in their unity of purpose.

Each Bynar has its own function in society. These functions are assigned at birth by the worldwide computer net.

Births occur asexually in a complex called a Crèche. They are strictly monitored and controlled.

People on other worlds often complain their planet is being built up and paved over. On Bynaeus everything **is** built up and paved over. Bynars do not like grass, trees and flowers but love metal and concrete. Their air recirculating plants create a clean atmosphere.

Hotels are indistinguishable from one another and have no names, just numbers. Tourists often become lost and wander unable to find where they are staying. To Bynars, forgetting a number is unthinkable.

Camus II

This is an ancient, abandoned world. The natives disappeared leaving behind a treasure throve of alien technology still being analyzed a century after its discovery by the Federation.

Dr. Janice Lester misused one of these devices in the 23rd Century. She harnessed deadly Celebium radiation to slay her fellow archeologists so she could use the secret of the Life-Entity Transfer device. This device exchanges consciousness between two bodies.

When Dr. Lester exchanged her mind with that of James T. Kirk, the process worked only temporarily. The ancients may never have intended the process to be permanent. Dr. Lester was sentenced to the Tantalus colony for the rest of her life.

The Life-Entity Transfer device was found in the Science Group Headquarters room. It has since been moved offworld for security purposes.

RELICS OF THE PAST In the century since Dr. Lester misused her discovery, scientists from every major world in the Federation have explored Camus II. Machines thought to be computers have been found, but they are so unlike known technology they cannot be used. A new interface is needed to access the information.

Devices from this world are inventive, and never lethal. It is as if weapons were either destroyed or never developed by that culture.

Large, colorful murals, painted with 12,000 years old pigments, stretch across caverns a hundred feet wide in a panorama of alien history. They tell how these beings created the wonders on that world and how they finally left to journey to distant stars.

It is still not clear whether the aliens of Camus II chose to migrate to a better world or were chased by a powerful threat. Scientists visit Camus II to explore technological riches greater than those of any other planet in the Alpha Quadrant.

An orbiting laboratory and temporary resident quarters has been established for visitors. Tourists are discouraged from visiting as they may accidentally damage precious artifacts.

Capella IV

[See FORBIDDEN ZONES]

Cardassia

This is the homeworld of the Cardassians, a warlike race who have a peace treaty with the Federation. They remain an unaligned world.

Cardassia was formally at war with the Federation several years ago, and while hostilities have ceased, relations remain strained. This is particularly true following the recent Cardassian attempt to annex Minos Corva. The attempt was thwarted by

Federation forces before the actual invasion could begin. Federation tourists are not welcomed on Cardassia.

Cardassians are similar in temperament to Romulans. They believe they are entitled to all they can take and do not treat subject peoples well. The Federation continues to debate the treatment of Bajor under the Cardassians. Cardassia rejects demands for reparations and proclaims accusations of war crimes to be fabrications.

Some Bajoran survivors were deliberately rendered speechless. They remain mute witnesses of the punishing shadow Cardassia once cast over Bajor.

Bajor accuses Cardassia of appropriating eight of the sacred Orbs ("Tears of the Prophets") found in space near Bajor. Cardassians took them to their homeworld for study where, it is presumed, they remain. The Cardassians have not pierced their secrets.

History records that Cardassia was a peaceful society until a military coalition seized power. The military insists they have improved the lifestyle of the average Cardassian, and starvation no longer exists. Others argue that this was accomplished by plundering other worlds.

The average Cardassian seems content under military rule. Recently, an anti-military underground began growing.

THE WORLD OF THE WARLORDS Cardassians are humanoids. They have rigid exoskeletons topped by a swatch of slick, black hair on their head.

The military runs the government. All officer names begin with their title—Gul. Their subordinates bear the title Glin. The Cardassian Guard is broken into divisions known as orders. Each order consists of three starships.

Dolamide is a principle ingredient of Cardassian weapons. It is also used for reactors, power generators and short range transports. Cardassia is developing Metagenic Weapons, and uses many other weapons. Anti-Lepton interference is used to jam subspace communications.

The Cardassians were initially accused of leaving an Aphasia device on Deep Space Nine. This device consisted of a small electronic circuit containing a diboridium power source that, when triggered, caused a plague of Aphasia aboard the former Cardassian space station.

Aphasia is "a perceptual dysfunction in which the oral and visual stimuli are incorrectly processed by the brain." The incubation period varies with each individual. It is a highly adaptive, airborne virus. Within 12 hours the virus attacks the nervous system creating a high fever that will cause death if not successfully treated.

Cardassia was innocent. The device had been planted nearly two decades before by Bajoran terrorists. It was left when the conflict ended. The Cardassians were highly offended by the accusation. They branded it another fraudulent attempt to discredit them. Only the use of Diboridium seemed to link the device to Cardassia.

THE RESOURCES OF THE OVERLORDS Cardassians use a Retinal scanner for security purposes. Their device, an MK-12, is equipped with an L-90 enhanced resolution filter. It scans the retina of the eye with a low level laser and reads the unique, recordable pattern.

Other Cardassian techniques include the use of Multi-phase currents on their turbo-lifts. The one they built on Deep Space Nine uses this method as do those on Cardassia.

Duranium is a metal used in construction, employed for its resistance to penetration by scanners. The Cardassians built Deep Space Nine's conduits with Duranium. Another Cardassian metal is Toranium, used on Deep Space Nine to line walls and bulkheads. This metal cannot be pierced by hand phasers, but can be cut with a bi-polar torch.

Cardassia has alliances with other worlds. There is a Cardassian military academy on Kora Two. Bellos Seven is the site of a Cardassian prison.

The Cardassians are allied with the Valerians. Because of this, Bajorans refuse to deal with Valerians and have pressured the Federation to keep them from the wormhole. Since Cardassians are not barred from using the wormhole, the Federation has refused to sanction the Valerians. Cardassians are also allied with Klaestron, another world Bajor does not maintain relations with.

Langour is a soothing Cardassian drink. It is pink in color, and very hard to find except on Cardassia.

Larish pie is a Cardassian delicacy that can be duplicated by replicators. Sem'hal Stew is a Cardassian dish enjoyed only by Cardassians because of its Yamok sauce.

NOT A NICE PLACE TO VISIT There is no tourist trade on this planet except from planets with an alliance with Cardassia. They accept none of the currency exchanges used by the Federation.

The Federation cannot guarantee the safety of anyone who visits Cardassia. Tourists often disappear on Cardassia. Their deserted, drifting vessels are found far enough from this world to give the government plausible deniability.

⊚CERBERUS II

This planet supplies an expensive, popular, illegal drug. Cerebran Youth Drug restores youth and vigor in most humanoids. This means of rejuvenation enjoys near mythical status.

Too big a dose taken too quickly can be fatal. Prolonged doses in prescribed amounts will safely restore youth. Few people can afford to indulge in this youth drug. Those who do often assume new identities.

Attempts have been made to synthesize the drug, but an ingredient unique to Cerberus II prevents it from being duplicated. This rare ingredient helps keep the cost of the drug high.

The people of this world are suspicious of strangers. They discourage tourism. There is a space port at the city of Sim, but it is for the use of natives. The city that surrounds it is a warren of alleys and tunnels in which a stranger is easily lost and disoriented. The residents are not friendly to strangers. Appointments with suppliers of the youth drug are made through an off world intermediary.

Cerberus is called the 'dark world,' not because of its heavy cloud cover or atmospheric anomalies, but because it does not welcome strangers. Offworlders always feel isolated.

⊚*CETI ALPHA V*

This formerly forbidden world was the planet of exile of Khan Noonian Singh, the notorious escaped criminal of the Eugenics Wars. Khan and his followers were consigned to live out their natural lives on this Class M world by Federation guidelines.

Years later, a comet destroyed Ceti Alpha VI and hurled Ceti Alpha V out of orbit. The new orbit, further away from the local sun, killed plant life and caused valleys and forests to become deserts. Only Khan and a handful of his people survived.

When a survey ship appeared, Khan seized its crew and escaped. He began a reign of terror while seeking revenge against James Kirk for abandoning him to his fate. After Khan's death, the Federation took a closer look at Ceti Alpha V and deemed it completely inhospitable.

DUNE WORLD Now a desert planet, the atmosphere is constantly wracked by violent storms. Sands covering the globe constantly move in a harsh, gritty sea. Although it would be possible to erect habitat domes, it has been deemed impractical. The planet has nothing valuable on its surface. It may one day be used as a penitentiary.

Creatures that live in the sand, notably the Ceti Eel, prey on hapless visitors. The eel's young crawl inside a person's head through the ear and remain wrapped around the cerebral cortex. The host goes mad with pain, finally becoming paralyzed. The adult Ceti Eel, although no larger than a human hand, can inflict a deadly bite. They are the only native life form known to have survived the hazardous climatic changes.

⊚*CHALNA*

This is the homeworld of the lion-like Chalnoth. They have long teeth, claws and short tempers. The carnivores are not social and often fight among themselves. It is surprising they developed an advanced technology and could apply for admission to Starfleet.

The Chalnoth are anarchists who lead a stress free life. Even one dissenter causes great disharmony.

Areas of the planet are settled by like-minded souls. One faction established contact with the Federation as representatives of their world.

Other areas are populated with residents who dislike dealing with offworld societies that do not follow an anarchistic philosophy. They feel every individual city-state on Chalna should agree on a plan for diplomatic contact before further talks with the Federation continue. The different groups clearly disagree. Meanwhile representatives continue negotiating with the Federation.

Tourists are welcome on Chalna, although they are lectured about the superiority of anarchism as practiced in the district visited. Hotels are run by the anarchists. They include mandatory lectures about the superiority of anarchism. They are amazed when visitors often reject their proselytizing.

CHANDRA FIVE

Visitors used to the hectic pace and intensity of other worlds will be either shocked or pleased by the way Chandrans live. Ritual is at the center of their society. Meeting new people is an event so important they have a three-day ritual greeting.

Chandrans have placid, untroubled minds. Their culture is thousands of years older than any other known in the Federation. Because of their lack of haste, they have only recently discovered space flight.

They engage in limited commerce with the Federation. Visitors looking for a slow paced week or month will discover that the Chandrans give new meaning to the word relaxed.

Hotels, such as the Royal Chandra Inn at the port city of Dronga, offer expansive rooms. The Chandrans perform a sleeping ritual in the tourist's rooms each night. This ritual lasts three hours.

CHERON

Civilization on this world was destroyed centuries ago due to racial strife. The ruins stand as a silent monument to how a world can destroy itself.

The few survivors are famous for their hatred. Bele and Lokai returned to Cheron a century ago to find their cities still in flames. The nearly inexhaustible elements that had provided miraculous power to satisfy their people's every want and need continue to burn.

This planet is a sad monument to both achievement and self-destruction. An orbiting space station provides facilities for visitors, primarily study groups from a variety of worlds. Several docugrams have been made of this world.

DEEP SPACE NINE

This space station, located near the planet Bajor at the mouth of the Wormhole to the Gamma Quadrant, is the only example of Cardassian space borne architecture readily accessible by way of Federation space. It has a grim history. Built by forced Bajoran labor, it served as the orbiting platform from which the Cardassians supervised their domination and exploitation of Bajor.

Now, in the wake of the Cardassian withdrawal, it is under Federation jurisdiction. Bajor is not yet a Federation member.

The space station regulates the flow of traffic entering and exiting the Wormhole to the Gamma Quadrant. Despite its limited defense capabilities and slight maneuverability, it has, so far, been able to hold its own, thanks to its shields and its sturdy construction of Cardassian duranium.

FOCUS ON:

DENEB IV: This world, the location of Farpoint Station, has emerged as a jewel in space. Traders and space travelers of every sort stop here. Farpoint Station even has a promotional cubicle on Deep Space Nine to inform visitors from the Gamma Quadrant.

Deneb IV features beautiful night skies. Atmospheric conditions make for cloudless skies at night that allow viewing of some of the most brilliant and complex star formations in any solar system. Because of the accident of fate that allows these constellations to be visible in such a startling array, the Bandi have been able to appeal to students of astronomy who have taken photographs seen in galleries far across the Federation. The sky over Deneb IV is reproduced in holoprograms available on countless worlds. Seeing the real thing holds a special wonder that cannot be duplicated.

Farpoint Station features modern hotels, the major one being the Polaris. Though only ten stories tall (buildings on Deneb IV have a height limit due to local ordinances), the hotel features a dome on the top level through which to view the vault of stars visible each night. Other hotels include the Orion Watch and Earthlight.

Restaurants feature the popular specialties from 20 Federation worlds, including food from Klinzai, served warm and squirming, of course. All forms of Federation currency exchange and barter are accepted.

Deep Space Nine is the perfect stepping stone to sightseeing in this rough-and-tumble sector of space designated as the Alpha Quadrant. Bajor is still a beautiful and fascinating world, rendered tragic by the ever-present scars of the recent Cardassian presence. Traffic through Deep Space Nine is increasing every year for the Bajoran Gratitude Ceremony as more and more tourists are coming to witness the intriguing rituals of this holiday against the spectacular backdrop of the Fire Caverns. Bajor's rich and varied religious heritage can be observed in the many shrines and monasteries that dot the land, still impressive despite wartime damage.

FACTS TO TAKE INTO ACCOUNT The space station is home to three hundred permanent and semipermanent residents, including Federation personnel, Bajoran crew and merchants, Ferengi traders and a remarkably diverse assortment of species.

One member of the crew, the security chief Odo, is a unique representative of his species, a shape shifter whose natural form is a protoplasmic liquid. He assumes a humanoid shape for most of each day-cycle. (Please note, however, that he does not demonstrate these abilities upon request— he serves in a vital security position and would be offended by such a request.)

Guest quarters are a sparse, designed with Cardassians in mind. They can be outfitted for comfort after a visit to the Promenade on the lower deck. It is possible to spend an entire vacation here, and leave with the feeling that you've visited at least a dozen worlds. The shops sell many goods, including Bajoran textiles and jewelry.

There is even a Cardassian tailor, the last Cardassian on the station. He is rumored to be quite good at his craft.

Traders and dealers (and more than a few con men) pass through the Promenade, in all shapes and sizes, on an almost daily basis. You might even see a stray visitor or two from the Gamma Quadrant, although to date they have been fairly rare.

The highlight of the Promenade is a wide-ranging establishment known as "Quark's Place." Quark himself, a perfect specimen of a Ferengi, is becoming a minor celebrity. He sometimes introduces himself as an "Honorary Nagus Emeritus." Quark offers the best stocked bar in the Alpha Quadrant, where only the most timid drink synthale. He also provides a full array of entertainments, including, the many games of his gambling rooms, including the highly popular Dabo, and the holosuites upstairs, which range from family entertainment to what Quark refers to as "more mature entertainments,"

Commander Benjamin Sisko welcomes visitors to Deep Space Nine, but requests they not interfere with the operations of the station. The space station can accommodate up to seven thousand people, although things start getting tight much above five thousand. The Promenade has a number of fine restaurants including one featuring authentic Klingon cuisine prepared by a typically surly Klingon chef—just don't let him serve you Gakh unless it's fresh and squirming.

In the middle of what many have called a backwater region of space, Deep Space Nine is a surprisingly bright tourist spot. Just don't schedule your trip during magnetic storm season.

DELPHI ARDU

This is a dead world with skies rent by lightning. The Class M planet is devoid of life and covered by rocky plains, a planet circling a cooling sun. It is a twilight world where night and day blend into one.

Ages ago this planet was part of the Tkon Empire. An ancient outpost still contains an android activated whenever anyone lands. It is the last functioning remnant of this defunct alien empire and guards a dead world.

Visitors are allowed. The Guardian of the planet knows what is happening in this era. There is nothing worth visiting, though. Delphi Ardu is very different from Risa and no plans have been made to use this bleak, uninviting piece of rock.

DELTA RANA IV

This planet in the Delta Rana system has a sad history. A Federation colony here was attacked and destroyed by a vessel from a previously unknown alien race.

The being disguised himself as a human and unleashed incredible powers. First it destroyed the alien ship, then all members of that alien race in the galaxy. In human form, the alien was married to an Earth woman who had died when the colony was destroyed.

The alien comes from a race of pacifists, although his species has never before or since made contact with the United Federation of Planets. As penance for his destructive act, the alien lives on the planet alone with a recreation of his wife and the house in which they had lived. The green patch of lawn around the tiny home is the only life remaining on Delta Rana IV, and that, too, is a recreation.

The Federation has chosen to honor his request and leave the planet alone.

DELTA VEGA

A Class M planet that is home to an old mining station manned only by robots. Ore ships arrive on this cold, inhospitable world every twenty years. Dust storms blow across its rocky plain.

Temperature controlled suits are recommended when walking on the surface. There is nothing to see.

If you must land on this world, the mining station is fully equipped with a communications center which will enable you to request aid. It has full life-support systems and guest accommodations.

DENEB IV

DENEB IV

The planet where Farpoint Station is located is inhabited by a race called the Bandi. They were severely sanctioned by the Federation over the incident involving the enslaving of an alien creature in their city.

The being possessed the power to replicate with its thoughts. The Bandi exploited this being until it escaped upon the arrival of its mate. Farpoint Station was constructed by the alien, and destroyed when the alien escaped.

The Bandi have rebuilt Farpoint Station with conventional means but the Federation keeps them under close watch. Slavery is expressly forbidden by the Federation. The Bandi citizens directly involved were demoted and reassigned to low level duty on the other side of the planet.

In the last seven years, Farpoint Station emerged as a jewel in space, a haven for traders and space travelers. Farpoint has a promotional cubicle on Deep Space Nine to inform visitors from the Gamma Quadrant of their world.

Deneb IV offers cloudless night skies and some of the most brilliant and complex star formations in any solar system. Deneb IV is a favorite attraction for students of astronomy. Photographs hang in galleries far across the Federation.

The sky over Deneb IV is often reproduced in holoprograms on countless worlds. No duplication can do justice to the real view.

Farpoint Station features modern hotels. The Polaris, though only ten stories tall (local ordinances limit the height of buildings on Deneb IV), features a dome on the top level. It offers a spectacular view of the vault of stars each night. Restaurants feature popular specialties from 20 primary Federation worlds. All forms of Federation currency and barter are accepted.

DENEVA

This key commercial planet houses a museum dedicated to its early settlers. Devastation befell them when a species of interplanetary parasites attacked, killing thousands.

The planet has fully recovered in the century since the invasion, but they no longer take their safety for granted. Quarantine procedures are required of all visitors. The Customs Office is located in a massive orbiting space station. The latest technology is employed to screen and scan passengers in the quickest and most inoffensive manner possible. They are then sped along to their destinations.

Cities have slidewalks and a subway system using special cars to speed tourists to a variety of mountain and seaside resorts. The Ariels, midrange mountains, are the most popular tourist attraction. Piz Gloria is a popular resort. Reservations should be made months in advance.

On the seashore at Renegade Bay, a vast metroplex and marina waits to service as many as three thousand visitors each night and up to five thousand spending the day. Renegade Bay has been described as a seaside "Disneyland" offering a wide variety of water sports and submarine activity.

All Federation currencies are accepted.

⊚ DYSON SPHERE

The Dyson Sphere is one of the most fantastic discoveries in the history of the Federation. Considered only theoretically possible until its discovery, this artificial construct in space is so large it defies description. It is an enclosed sphere built around a star. The sphere is 180 million miles in diameter. The star is at its center, 90 million miles from the perimeter.

The abandoned structure is many thousands of years old, predating even the oldest advanced civilization in the Federation. The Dyson Sphere was abandoned because the cooling of the star made it impractical to live on the sphere.

Why it was not disassembled and reconstructed around another star has never been determined. It is possible the civilization that constructed it was able to replicate matter making moving the sphere unnecessary.

The identity of the builders, and the exact age of the Dyson Sphere is unknown. The fate of the builders is also unknown.

The sphere can be visited and studied, but entering it is considered hazardous as a starship can be caught inside. The sphere cannot be pierced by the strongest phasers, which is just one of many aspects of the construct now being studied by teams of Federation scientists.

Several holographs have been composed about the sphere and many scientists have chosen to devote their lives to the study of this unique artificial phenomenon.

EKOS

 EKOS

This planet has a sister planet named Zeon. They were at Ekos is located in the star system M43 Alpha. It war a century ago. The conflict has long since been resolved.

Ekos is an example of the reason for the Prime Directive. A century ago, Federation historian John Gill interfered with the developing culture. He introduced Nazism in the mistaken belief it would strengthen the culture.

Instead it followed the same path it followed on Earth in the mid-20th Century. The absolute power given the government soon corrupted it. John Gill was elevated to Fuhrer but drugged by his deputy, Melakon.

Melakon wanted to rule both Ekos and Zeon. When John Gill revealed the truth, he was assassinated by Melakon, and a successful coup took place.

The Federation helped remove all influences brought to the culture by John Gill. Memories of the contamination could not be completely expunged. A coalition of the governments of Zeon and Ekos was formed and peace has reigned ever since.

EKOS TODAY The two governments shared technology and resources to the betterment of both worlds. Ekos discovered that the Rubindium crystals found in abundance on their world are invaluable for electronics. This created a basis for technological advances on both worlds.

Today they are thriving civilizations that welcome tourists. There are numerous four star hotels in the capitol city of Gillton. The primary hotels are the Kannorm Spire and the Azrael Travelodge, which is far more expansive than its modest name denotes.

Both Ekos and Zeon are warm worlds rich in plant and animal life, none of which are hazardous to humans. Both planets are 3,000 miles in diameter with high, diaphanous clouds girdling their equators. Summers are long and winters are short.

The past problems on Ekos are now nothing more than a historical footnote.

 ELAS

The sister worlds of Elas and Troyius are found in the Tellun Star System. They did not always enjoy the peaceful co-existence they live in now.

A century ago these worlds were engaged in a bitter conflict, settled only by uniting their ruling families. The King of Troyius married the Dohlmann of Elas, bringing peace.

The worlds had newly achieved space flight when they contacted the Federation. There was a claim on the region by the Klingon Empire, which was disputed by the Federation, representing Troyius and Elas.

When the Federation discovered Elas was rich in Radans, raw dilithium crystals, the Klingons' true interest became clear. The poor world became a wealthy source of power crystals.

Troyius is more pleasant than Elas. The latter world suffers a harsh climate and is very rocky with scattered oasis where subterranean rivers come to the surface. Similar in size, Troyius is more tropical than the cold, stormy, windswept Elas.

This doesn't keep tourists away. Males are the majority of visitors to Elas. The women of this world have a peculiar biological trait. Their tears are a powerful aphrodisiac. The antidote was discovered long ago, but not all males want one.

The women are very popular. A true aphrodisiac is rare in the universe.

A shore leave center in the seacoast city of Elaan spans twenty miles square and can accommodate thousand of visitors. Hotels accommodating humanoids and non-humanoids are abundant. It is rumored the women of Elas do not discriminate against beings who are totally alien in appearance.

⌀ELBA II

This planet formerly housed an asylum for the criminally insane inside a life support dome. Its atmosphere is poisonous to all known life forms, making escape impossible without outside assistance.

The penitentiary was closed a century ago when a new medication was discovered to cure the physiological imbalances of the inmates. Today the dome remains, a mute reminder of the past.

The uninhabited dome has working automated life support systems, communications and a transporter. It is a haven for vessels forced down on this deadly world.

⌀EMINIAR VII

Eminiar VII is located in the NGC 321 star system. It was at war with its neighboring planet, Vendikar (formerly known as Eminiar III), for 500 years at the time the Federation made initial contact a century ago.

The two worlds had reduced warfare to clean, non-destructive computer strikes. People designated as being in the "strike zone" were required to report for termination in euthanasia centers within 24 hours.

The worlds attempted to drag the Federation into the conflict by designating the visiting starship as a target "hit" by a mythical fusion bomb. The starship captain responded by destroying the wargame computer to save his crew.

Eminiar VII and Vendikar suddenly faced returning to destruction on a planetary scale. The governments quickly struck a peace accord.

Today the worlds live in harmony. They compete only for the tourist dollar.

look here Vendikar is the lusher of the two worlds. Its inhabitants more carefully developed their world, setting aside vast wilderness areas for future generations to enjoy.

The people of Eminiar VII rarely left their world as they grew to maturity. The population swelled. Cities grew across the planet until virtually everything was covered with beautiful architecture.

Striking color schemes were employed to relieve the tedium of urban sprawl. Each city became a unique artistic delight. Craftsmen from many worlds added individual touches. The world evolved in a positive way.

The people of Eminiar VII do not feel victimized by their population. They enjoy their glittering, paved over planet.

◉ EXCALBIA

This world is covered with active volcanoes. It is home to a non-human native life form based on carbon.

The Federation made first contact with Excalbia a century ago. The Excalbians scanned the vessel and experimented with the concepts of good and evil, something new to their world. Contact ended in the Federation's favor.

The incredibly alien nature of the inhabitants of Excalbia makes communication difficult. Federation diplomats have often tried.

Excalbians possess great power and a vast technology which they refuse to show to off worlders. Its effects are readily apparent. They scan approaching ships with a sensor so powerful it instantly reads computer banks and the minds of beings aboard the ship.

The volcanic world is inhospitable to most life forms. It is covered with fields of molten lava.

The Starfleet vessel which made initial contact reported that the Excalbians could turn a thousand kilometer area into a Class M planet. This led many to wonder whether the volcanic surface is an illusion, just as the rock-like nature of the beings may not be their true form.

This is not a forbidden world, but visitors are discouraged unless they are Federation diplomatic personnel or going there to study the world. The ambient temperature of 300 degrees Celsius does not make this planet attractive for shore leave.

◉ EXO III

This icy world is covered with glaciers and snow. Deep beneath its surface lurks the remains of an ancient civilization discovered more than a century ago by Dr. Roger Korby.

This civilization built androids so advanced they could pass as human. The androids dwarfed the power of their masters, The Old Ones. They finally destroyed them.

The civilization slowly died. When Roger Korby discovered the remains in caverns deep beneath the surface, he also found working technology. This included an ancient android still functioning after thousands of years.

Dr. Korby pierced the secret of this technology. He created android duplicates, including one of himself. Sadly, in transferring his intelligence into an android body, he lost touch with his humanity. He finally chose to destroy himself and took the secret of the ancient technology with him.

Today Exo III remains an archeological paradise. It has been explored and studied over the last century.

The small world has been in an ice age for centuries. Archeologists are the principal visitors, but ski teams from Terra junket to this world, indulging in hundred mile ski marathons. They also engage in the modern equivalent of what was called "Extreme Skiing" in the 20th century. Falling off mountains is no longer a hazard, though, due to emergency anti-grav devices.

 **FERENGI**

The Ferengi, those dwarfish, large-eared businessmen, are perhaps the most colorful characters you are likely to meet in your galactic travels. Many unusual corners of the universe can be reached only with assistance from Ferengi travel agents. Be warned—their primary belief is summed up in their First Rule of Acquisition: "Once you have their money, you never give it back."

If you find yourself stranded in the Gamma Quadrant for three weeks, waiting for return passage through the Wormhole, you won't get even a partial refund from the Ferengi who told you the stopover would take three hours at the most.

While any Ferengi will sell you passage to just about anywhere, no one has ever visited their home world. An ancient joke maintains that the Ferengi spread so far across space in their quest for gold-press latinum they've forgotten where their home world is. An equally old jibe is probably much closer to the truth: their home world is where they keep all the wealth they've acquired, and they're not about to let anyone near the fruit of their labors. This is also where they keep their women.

CULTURAL QUIRKS Humans are amazed to discover the Ferengi embody the worst of what Earth called "sexism" a few centuries ago. Ferengi keep their women totally isolated from the male concerns of business and acquisition. Treated as sex objects, they are not even allowed to wear clothes, so they can be available for the satisfaction of their mates at any time.

Ferengi males are noted for their sex drive, and are wildly attracted to females of all known humanoid species except Klingons. Klingons look down on Ferengi as mere shopkeepers, while Ferengi consider Klingons the worst people to do business with.

While many find Ferengi behavior obnoxious, it must be admitted that many Ferengi males are remarkably successful in their indiscriminate sexual pursuits. Another long-standing Ferengi joke bears on this matter, but it's not suited to the pages of a general publication such as this one.

A Ferengi's ear lobes, called Oo-Mox in their native tongue, are a primary erogenous zone; sensuous manipulation of the lobes, much favored by Ferengi males, is also called Oo-Mox.

Ferengi pride themselves on their skill at business. Acquisition is the core of their philosophy and lives. This often puts them at odds with Federation and other authorities; they are involved in illegal commerce, but only because they are being true to the highest ideals of their own culture. Getting around other peoples' rules is a challenge the Ferengi relish.

Some Ferengi are brash in their efforts, such as the ill-fated group of Ferengi pirates who attempted to hijack the flagship of Starfleet, the Enterprise, a few years ago. Such acts are generally regarded as folly by craftier Ferengi who rely on wiles, craft and deceit.

FERENGI

In all honesty, such attitudes derive more from the failure of the plan than from its aggressive nature. For the Ferengi, the ends certainly justify the means. The Ferengi have developed the means to protect themselves in their many years of galactic exploitation. Energy whips, sophisticated starships— all of these, and more, have been used by the Ferengi.

PREPARE TO BE SURPRISED The humanoid Ferengi have many unusual characteristics that set them apart. They are shorter than the galactic average, and are marked by their immense ear lobes— both staples of the regrettable anti-Ferengi humor that seems to pervade the known universe.

Their brains are their truly distinguishing feature. Composed of four sections, they process information in ways that baffle researchers from other planets. From a Ferengi viewpoint, there is one highly beneficial side effect of their unique brains: telepathic races like the Betazoids simply cannot read even the faintest emotion or thought from a Ferengi. This doesn't bother the Ferengi one bit. Their less intelligent relatives, the Dopterians, also are closed to the prying of telepaths and empaths.

Not all Ferengi live up (or down) to the common stereotype of them as greedy profiteers. Always be prepared to be surprised by a Ferengi. They have a fairly advanced scientific community. One Ferengi scientist, Doctor Reyga, single-handedly revolutionized metaphasic field technology, developing techniques capable of creating force fields strong enough to protect spacecraft from the intense heat of a stellar corona.

Most Ferengi you encounter will be out to get their hands on your credits, goods or gold-press latinum, so be extremely cautious in all dealings with them, even though most Ferengi are incredibly honest and would never dream of defrauding anyone.

(This is a good time to point out that this publication is in no way affiliated with any Ferengi consortium, organization or individual. Really.)

Competition between Ferengi is intense. There is very little in the way of formal education; young Ferengi are pawns in the business schemes of their elders, ultimately left to fend for themselves as businessmen, sinking or swimming according to their abilities and what they have learned the hard way. It takes a remarkable Ferengi to rise to the ultimate power in their culture— the position of Grand Nagus. Let there be no doubt— the Ferengi work hard, and the Grand Nagus hasn't had a vacation in eighty-three years.

THE JOY OF ACQUISITION The current Grand Nagus, Zek, tested his son's worthiness by faking his own death and appointing an obscure shopkeeper as his successor. The turnout of this affair is revealing: the son undertook to assassinate and replace the new Nagus, when what the real Nagus was looking for was someone crafty enough to assume real power while using the shopkeeper as a frontman puppet. This seems to suggest, to outsiders, that Ferengi who use force to acquire profits are looked down upon by their society; the highest ideals are wheeling, dealing and general sneakiness.

They do have unusual weapons, such as locator bombs (composed of the explosives argine and sorium) which lock on to their intended victim's pheromones. Perhaps there is more than one school of thought regarding acquisition in the Ferengi philosophy.

The Ferengi are so busy acquiring things, it's hard to see when they have time to enjoy their acquisitions— and many of them seem not to enjoy life at all.

Visitors to Quark's Place on the Deep Space Nine relate that the proprietor of that establishment, the temporary Nagus mentioned above, has a flair for living that makes a visit to the distant Bajoran region worthwhile despite the general poverty of tourists *leaving* Quark's. Many are surprised to find that Ferengi lokar beans are quite pleasant to most palates. Live, chilled tube grubs, an acquired taste, are another matter entirely. Ferengi synthale is particularly good— but if you are unwise enough to imbibe a pink Ferengi Starduster, don't be surprised to wake up and discover that you've been cleaned out at the Dabo tables.

In short, you are quite likely to encounter Ferengi just about anywhere but Romulus, the Klingon home world, and Vulcan, a place the Ferengi avoid due to the painfully non materialistic nature of the inhabitants. When dealing with the Ferengi, it is wise to remember an Earth saying nearly two and a half thousand years old: *Caveat Emptor—* Let The Buyer Beware!

◉ *Gamma Canaris n*

[by Kay Doty]

The colorful landscapes of Gamma Canaris N range from red clay rock formations to deep green seas. It is breath-taking viewed at close range, and awe-inspiring viewed against the changing background of the blue-to-pink-to-purple sky.

The people of Gamma Canaris N are as varied as the landscape. Terrans, Andorians, Angosians and Rigellians work together in business and the for the betterment of their adopted world. They each still maintain their own culture, customs and traditions.

There are ten 25-day months in a year, for a total of 275 (Earth) days. Each day is 21.5 hours. Temperatures vary by ten degrees between the world's two seasons. The average temperature is 51 C during the day, and 40 C at night. The Rain Phase occurs during the first three months of the year, chiefly at the poles. Natural canals carry pure water to the continents.

Gamma Canaris N is not round. In the distant past a huge object, perhaps a meteor or comet, struck the planet on the continent of Alpha near the northern pole. It gouged a hole 13,127 kilometers long and 9,082 wide. The hole eventually filled with warm water, creating Lake Kirk.

GEOGRAPHY Alpha's northern perimeter is located near the polar cap. This causes heavy rainfall on Alpha, providing water for a large expanse of deciduous trees. This forest is a favorite recreation area. Visitors camp, hike and fish in the streams, but no hunting of the 117 varieties of wild fauna is allowed. No admittance to the polar cap is permitted.

The greatest attraction is Lake Kirk. The lake is surrounded by millions of small, sharp lava rocks, forcing visitors to wear specially designed shoe-boots even when swimming. Regular street shoes are prohibited. The required footwear may be obtained in the nearby village of McCoy's town.

Most people live in the center of Alpha in the World Capitol, Hedford. While much of the area is a rolling plain, valleys provide an agreeable climate for small vegetable and fruit farms.

PLANETARY FEATURES The Galileo and April Mountain chains lie to the south, surrounding an arid area of great rose-colored sand dunes, some 6,000 kilometers high. Beyond rise the red rock formations known and admired by travelers throughout the galaxy. Fields of multi-colored flowers cover the mountains.

The continent of Betta might be on another world. It is completely unlike her larger sister. There is also much for the visitor to enjoy. There are long expanses of rose tinted sand along the shores of the Great Sea. They do not require special footwear.

The sprawling Markkys cattle and horse ranch is the main attraction. It covers the southern hemisphere, bordered by the Canaris Archeology Pits to the north. The ranch features 92 isolated cabins offering privacy and a taste of rural life. Riding horses are available and campouts can be arranged. Tours of the Canaris Pits are open to the public during all except the rain months.

Betta has two small villages. One is named Pittown, the other, Supply-Town. The latter is located on the ranch.

HISTORY The colony on Gamma Canaris N was founded by Zefram Cochrane and his wife Nancy Hedford-Cochrane on Earth date 2267. Cochran's early life remained a mystery at his insistence, until after his death in 2341. He had given permission for his story to be engraved on his memorial plate.

The entire galaxy was surprised to learn that this quiet, unobtrusive man not only discovered the warp drive, but many other inventions as well. He single-handedly improved space travel. Most believed the great inventor had died nearly two hundred years earlier.

THE TRUTH At age 87, tired and ill, Cochrane secretly filled his small space craft with his most prized possessions and left his Alpha Centauri home. He wanted to die in the space he loved. This was not to be.

His tiny ship was pulled from space to Gamma Canaris N by a cloud-like creature known only as The Companion. This entity sustained him for 150 years, rejuvenating him to the approximate age of forty.

The Companion eventually realized The Man was lonely. When a shuttlecraft entered the system, she pulled it off course to Gamma Canaris N. Captain James Kirk, First Officer Spock and Doctor Leonard McCoy of the starship Enterprise, and a very ill Assistant Federation Commissioner Nancy Hedford were aboard the shuttle.

Before the Starfleet officers could escape, Hedford lapsed into a near-death coma. The Companion, wishing to be human and touch The Man she loved, occupied Hedford's body. The Commissioner was cured, but merged with The Companion. It was impossible for her to leave the planet. Cochrane, who had fallen in love with Nancy at first sight, chose to stay with her.

As the Starfleet officers left, Cochrane asked them never to reveal that he still lived. Kirk promised—and kept his word. He secretly sent a supply ship carrying tapes, sen-

FOCUS ON:

GAMMA HYDRA IV: Atmospheric conditions make it a world without storms, a rare planet indeed. This has brought meteorologists from many worlds. They study the atmosphere hoping to learn the natural balance achieved on Gamma Hydra IV.

This world has raised relaxation to a high art. Vacation is a year round activity. Luxury hotels include the Maxwell Arms, the Murdock Skyspire and Lyon Square. Each offers rooms ranging in size from 2,000 to 4,000 square feet. All forms of Federation exchange accepted.

sors, communication equipment, building materials, a case of Saurian Brandy, a wide variety of seeds and tree saplings. Kirk displayed his wry sense of humor by including four fig trees.

From time to time, other supplies, including news tapes and newly developed seedlings, were beamed to the planet by passing ships. No explanations were ever given to the ship's captains.

A COLONY IS ESTABLISHED With a new life and new responsibilities, Nancy and Zefram searched for ways to improve their world. Adding native stone to Kirk's building materials, Zefram built a science lab. For the first time in over 150 years, he returned to his life's work. Nancy began a journal of their life together.

Nancy happily busied herself creating the first real home she had ever known. Nearly a year after her arrival on Gamma Canaris N, she told Zefram he would have to abandon his lab work to build a nursery.

Five years and three children later, the couple decided the lonely planet life that they enjoyed would not always be suitable for their children. The children were beginning to need playmates. A certain Admiral, once an Enterprise captain, received a coded message stating that Gamma Canaris N was opening its doors to limited immigration.

Months passed before a ship carrying 114 residents from Rigel VII left orbit and skidded to a landing near the Galileo Mountains. The travelers were exhausted and one of their group had died, but they were happy to find a haven.

A deteriorating political system and threatening world war had prompted their escape from their homeworld. As storm clouds gathered, they secreted supplies and personal possessions aboard an old freighter, the Raptor. The captain shared the group's concerns. He quietly prepared his vessel for their journey.

One stormy night, during a riot, the determined group boarded the Raptor and silently slipped away into space. The Raptor's commander, Captain Gurnik, had heard of the Gamma Canaris N invitation.

A CROSS-SECTION   Other groups came to make Gamma Canaris N their home. They included nine Andorians from Epsilon Indii VIII, looking for adventure in a new world.

Four families from Angosia III, tired of the decades-long war ravishing their world, made a desperate bid for freedom in a government warship. Their departure did not go unnoticed and they were fired upon, but eluded the Angosian pilots.

Cochrane was astonished that their torpedo damaged ship could navigate. The escapees crash-landed with only minor injuries to the passengers. The ship had fought its last battle.

The Angosians had tried to reach a Federation Space Station to defect. They liked this developing world, pleased by the warm greetings, and decided to call it home.

The gallant ship that had carried them to a new life was carefully dismantled. The parts were used to build homes and a small gift shop where they would eventually sell hand-crafted Angosian wares.

From time to time unknown ships beamed down passengers looking for a place to make a new start. All new arrivals were joyfully greeted and helped to find a place for themselves in the growing community.

BUILDING THEIR DREAMS One of the most enthusiastic greetings, accorded by the predominately male population, went to an Orion slaver ship. Twenty-one green-skinned slave girls, determined to find liberation from their life of bondage, had taken their captain and navigator hostage. They demanded to be taken to a world where they could be free.

The girls were readily accepted, and within a month seven marriages were celebrated. The two kidnapped officers, knowing they would be severely punished, if not murdered, for their laxness in allowing the ship to be hijacked, elected to stay as well.

Another arrival would do much to expand the economy of Gamma Canaris N. Former Starfleet lieutenant Jack-David Markkys came alone in a luxury yacht. He was wealthy, and loved adventure and wide open country. He had found service on a starship too confining. Resigning his commission after his enlistment term ended, he bought the yacht and went in search of a new life.

Gamma Canaris N answered his dream. He established his ranch on the then uninhabited continent of Betta, ordered top breeds from across the galaxy, including a dozen head of cattle from Earth. A year later, he began supplying meat products to Alpha at a price much lower than imports. It was Markkys who made the archeological find, donated the pits to the government, and paid to have a team of Federation scientists work the pits.

Markkys was content. He worked hard, watched his business grow and enjoyed many friendships. His contentment became complete the day he married Zefram and Nancy's daughter, Nancy-Anne.

POINTS OF INTEREST The new immigrants needed housing and public buildings. Cochrane made one unbreakable rule: no two structures, including homes, could be exactly alike. The rule has been carefully adhered to, making Gamma Canaris N a worldwide architectural showplace.

The SEAT-OF-GOVERNMENT HOUSE, a triangular building located in the city center, was constructed while Nancy Hedford-Cochrane was serving as Gamma Canaris N's first governor. Many of Gamma Canaris N's earliest records, documents and artifacts are on display in the rotunda.

THE CLOCK TOWER is a circular edifice designed by Cochrane to stand tall enough to allow two lighted clock faces to be visible. The jagged top and carefully placed hand carved openings allow sunlight to strike the back of the clocks to determine the exact time. A reservoir coupled with a resonator stores energy during the day, continuing the clock's operation during the night. A spiral staircase winds around the inside of the building, allowing visitors to reach a viewing platform twelve meters from the top. A high window presents a panoramic view of the surrounding landscape

Other points of interest in the city include the modern SCIENCE LABORATORY, constructed to include Cochrane's original workshop, now a museum named (by Cochrane) Spock's Inspiration. Many shops, restaurants, beverage-houses, theaters and chapels abound throughout the city. Each has its own particular design, merchandise and cuisine, determined by the owner's species.

Visitors and residents alike agree that the MEMORIAL PALACE is the most beautiful structure on Gamma Canaris N. It is also the largest. Built of the rare white stones found near the eastern shore of Betta, the wide, rectangular Palace has a transparent roof that extends upward at an angle until the two sides meet and are joined by a golden ridge. This is the home of the dead.

LOCAL CUSTOMS Gamma Canaris N is a small world. It does not bury its dead but practices cremation and allows the ashes to drift out to sea. Every being leaves a personal testimonial inscribed on burnished silver-gray plates attached to the Memorial Palace wall. The Palace is located seven kilometers from Hedford in one corner of the TREES OF THE GALAXY PARK.

During his early lonely years on the unpopulated world, Cochrane began collecting and transplanting native trees and wildflowers to an open area near his home. He later added bushes and vegetables, calling the spot, "My Garden." Immigrants and Kirk's secret supply shipments brought plants and seeds from many other worlds. Eventually My Garden became Trees of the Galaxy Park, a beautiful setting where visitors could relax on white stone benches.

The modern shuttle-port and beam-down arena provide convenient, safe arrivals and departures. Long visitor counters provide prompt service for those wishing information, lodging, ground car rentals or transportation into the city. Currency exchange kiosks are located in several areas of the terminal.

◉ *Gamma Hydra IV*

This Class M world is located near Starbase 10. This planet's colony was wiped out by a plague brought by a passing comet a century ago. This plague caused accelerated aging. Although a cure was finally discovered, most of the colonists had succumbed before their plight was discovered by the Federation.

It took a long time before the Federation established another colony, even after it was determined the comet would not return. Starfleet studied the comet for several months before vaporizing it.

FACTS TO TAKE INTO ACCOUNT Gamma Hydra IV is a pleasant world with a temperate climate. Winters range from mild to non-existent.

Wealthy residents of Federation worlds established an exclusive colony dubbed the Riviera of space. Hundred foot long yachts ply the crystal oceans surrounding the main continent of Abraxis. Anti-grav ships coast through the clouds over the floating city Icarus.

This is a rare world without storms. Meteorologists from other worlds study the atmosphere to better manage the weather on their own planets.

Relaxation has been raised to a high art on this world. Luxury hotels include the Maxwell Arms, the Murdock Skyspire and Lyon Square. Their rooms range in size from 2,000 to 4,000 square feet.

All forms of Federation exchange are accepted.

Not for the budget minded.

⊚ *Gamma Quadrant*

This is an area of space 70 thousand light-years from Federation space. A journey to this area was once considered impossible for anything other than a sleeper ship or a Generation ship. Even the fastest starship took 67 years to get there.

The discovery of the Tetryon Wormhole near Bajor changed all this. A trip to the Gamma Quadrant is now no more difficult than one to most Federation worlds.

The wormhole always opens at the same point in the Gamma Quadrant, five light-years from the Idran system. This star system consists of two type "O" stars but has no Class M worlds.

GATEWAY TO NEW WORLDS Two years have elapsed since the discovery of the "Bajoran wormhole." Little is yet known about the Gamma Quadrant. One fact has emerged, the existence of a shadowy group known as "The Dominion."

Visitors from the Gamma Quadrant call "The Dominion" the real power behind the thrones of countless worlds. Startling evidence of this occurred when three million refugees emerged through the wormhole, abandoning their world after the Dominion took over.

These people were slaves until the Dominion conquered their masters. The Dominion allowed them to flee, indicating that it may not be a threat to civilized peoples.

Prior to the Bajoran Wormhole, all information about the Gamma Quadrant had come from the 22nd Century probe known as Quadros-One. Since travel through the wormhole has begun, the Federation has made contact with the Wadi and the planet of Rakhar.

The Wadi consider nothing more important than playing games. Upon arriving on Deep Space Nine they were less interested in opening diplomatic discussions with Commander Sisko than examining the gaming establishments.

RAKHAR—A CRUEL WORLD Rakhar doesn't want contact with the Federation other than to retrieve an escaped political dissident named Croden. He was reportedly lost en route to Rakhar.

This harsh world follows strict laws and exhibits intolerance of anyone who questions the status quo. They are brutal to those who challenge authority and track down anyone who flees. They believe exiles could band together and attempt to return.

Relations between the Federation and Rakhar are not good. Travel to Rakhar is discouraged because of the risk of violating one of Rakhar's 7,000 Rules of Submission.

The Leader of the Nehelik province on the Planet Rahkar is called the Exarch. There are no trials for the accused, only swift punishment.

Other regions in the Gamma Quadrant include the Varath system with its ancient statues. The Denkiri Arm was discovered when the Barzan Wormhole temporarily linked the Alpha Quadrant with the Gamma Quadrant.

The Gamma Quadrant is an important source of the substance deuridium. Rich deposits of Miszindol ore have been discovered on the planet Stakoron Two.

THE THRILL OF DISCOVERY Some regions in the Gamma Quadrant have been mapped and marked as hazardous, such as the Chamra Vortex. It contains many volatile pockets of an explosive substance called Toh Maire. This area is located in an asteroid belt.

A unique "shape-shifting" stone was discovered in this asteroid belt. The only thing similar to this strange object is Constable Odo of Deep Space Nine, the shape-shifter of unknown origin. His race may be somewhere in the Gamma Quadrant.

Explorers of this region brought back many highly prized unusual artifacts, including a strange geode. It wreaked havoc on the energy fields of Deep Space Nine until the geode was revealed as an alien egg. It hatched releasing a winged energy entity that returned through the wormhole to the Gamma Quadrant.

FOCUS ON:

SPOTLIGHT ON GAMMA CANARIS N: The main attractions on Betta are the sprawling Markkys cattle and horse ranch. Covering the southern hemisphere, the ranch is bordered by the Canaris Archeology Pits to the north. The ranch features 92 isolated cabins for visitors who wish privacy and a taste of rural life. Riding horses are available and campouts can be arranged.

Tours of the Canaris Pits are open to the public during all except the rain months. Betta has two small villages. One is named, appropriately enough, Pittown. The other, Supply-Town, is located on the ranch.

Visitors and residents agree that the Memorial Palace is the most beautiful structure on Gamma Canaris N. It is also the largest. Built of the rare white stones found near the eastern shore of Betta, the wide, rectangular Palace has a transparent roof that extends upward at an angle. The two sides meet and are joined by a golden ridge. This is the home of the dead.

Drolock was The Prime Asemety of the Verath System during the 19th Dynasty. A statue of this ancient figure was discovered in the Gamma Quadrant and brought back for study. This civilization reached its zenith thirty thousand years ago when it flourished in two dozen star systems connected by a tight trade and communications network.

Archeological exploration is unrestricted on many unclaimed worlds in the Gamma Quadrant. Early excursions indicate cultures flourished in this region millions of years ago.

MYSTERIES IN SPACE One early contact in the Gamma Quadrant was between a Klingon survey ship and energy spheres responsible for the destruction of the Saltah'na. The spheres, named Thalmerite Devices by the Klingons, have since been studied and neutralized.

Another race in the Quadrant breeds intelligent beings called Tosks to lead their masters on exciting hunts. The Tosks die when cornered. For a Tosk to be captured alive is a great dishonor. It would result in a life of public display as an object of humiliation.

An inhabited moon lies .35 light years from the Wormhole in a binary star system. This prison planet is protected by an elaborate network of security satellites. Inmates are kept alive to serve extremely long terms through the use of an artificial microbe. The microbe will bring a being back to life, but their body becomes permanently dependent on the microbe for all cellular functions. If they leave the moon, they die.

GUARDIANS OF THE WORMHOLE The artificial Bajoran Wormhole provides a gateway to the Gamma Quadrant. The aliens who made the Tetryon wormhole live inside it. When they met a representative of the Federation, Commander Benjamin Sisko, they gave permission for the wormhole to be used for transportation to and from the Gamma Quadrant.

The Wormhole is stable due to a lack of the residence waves ordinarily found in wormholes. The opening and closing of the Bajoran wormhole is accompanied by a neutrino disturbance. Passage through the wormhole is possible by using impulse power.

The beings who created the wormhole are a previously unknown race. They had no idea of linear time until it was explained to them by Benjamin Sisko. The Bajorans refer to these beings as the "Prophets" and think they are gods.

The Gamma Quadrant holds many unknown wonders and threats. Only trade ambassadors journey there unaccompanied by Federation Starfleet escorts. Doubtless one day an entire book will be written on the Gamma Quadrant. In the meantime, it is best to leave the discoveries to the experts.

GAMMA TRIANGULI VI

[See FORBIDDEN ZONES]

 GIDEON

The people of this world achieved breakthroughs in biological and environmental engineering, including a germ-free atmosphere and an extended life span. Their bodies regenerate lost cells making them effectively immortal. This led to overpopulation.

This was once the most overpopulated planet known to the Federation. A century ago the legendary starship captain James T. Kirk was lured there on the pretext of opening a dialogue between Gideon and the Federation. Instead Kirk was kidnapped so that dormant disease organisms in his blood could be isolated and introduced into the general population. Because the people of Gideon are opposed to birth control, this external solution was needed to control the size of the population.

The disease organisms created plagues against which the race had no defense. Paradise became a charnel house, but years passed before the population was reduced to a manageable size.

MODERN WONDERS That decision made a century ago has become controversial. The people can no longer imagine why the suicide pact was needed. Although their beliefs do not preclude suicide, such massive and haphazard death seems almost unbelievable. Holotapes show the Gideon that led to the desperate decision.

Until the great plague, the word "alone" had become an abstraction. Today privacy is cherished. Everyone has a meditation chamber in their home where they spend time alone each day. This has contributed to the mental well-being of the population.

Gideon welcomes tourists with fine resorts, but immigrating to this world is difficult. They are watchful of the size of their population and concerned with resources and potential growth. Immigrants must have a needed skill or contribution to make to Gideon society. Even then the number is limited by how many Gideon natives choose to emigrate to another world.

This world remained a paradise even during the worst days of population strife. Now it can be appreciated by everyone since it has been opened to visitors.

The best hotels include the Huxley World Center and the Aldous Arms.

All Federation currencies are gratefully accepted.

GRAVES WORLD

This isolated desolate planet is far off normal travel lanes. It was once the home of Dr. Ira Graves and his assistant, Kareen Brianon. A brilliant cyberneticist, Graves was the only known equal to Dr. Noonian Soong. In face, he was Soong's mentor.

When Graves died Brianon left Graves World to pursue her career elsewhere. Graves World was opened to development and colonization.

Temperatures are chilly and rainfall is sparse. Plants are limited to lichens. Dr. Graves had a lavish domed structure built in which to do his work. It was funded by several different conglomerates.

Today the planet is abandoned.

 **HALKAN**

The small, green world is plagued by frequent ionic storms. Violent storms strike without warning with spectacular displays of lightning flashing across the sky. The storms cause few problems on the surface, but can play havoc with an orbiting starship. Use of transporters is not recommended during ionic storms.

THE STORMY WORLD OF PEACE The planet of peace provides an example for all worlds. If the Organians symbolize moving beyond war, the Halkans demonstrate that a race need not evolve into disembodied entities to make moral decisions and understand actions have consequences.

Halkans are devoted to non-aggression. They refuse to profit from selling dilithium crystals to the Federation because the crystals can power vessels of war, violating their philosophy of non-violence. This philosophy directs all their actions. They would die as a race rather than wage war.

The Federation preserves order with rules, regulations and justified force; Halkans and Organians are the peacemakers of the galaxy. It is said that priests come to Halkan to learn non-aggression.

FOCUS ON:

HAVEN: The Wedding World. The best hotels are the Skyway Chapel, the Arch of Wonder and the Hilton Milespire (with the finest penthouse in the solar system).

Private aircars are available for rent. They operate on solar power and can circle the globe. Controls may be set to return the vehicles automatically to their point of departure at any time. A driver cannot get lost. The skies are often filled with belts of carefully guided aerial traffic. No accidents have occurred in 25 years.

Restaurants include the "Gakh of Glory," serving Klingon food prepared only by four star Klingon chefs (who guarantee that their Gakh is served alive and squirming). "Saurian Andy" is a favorite eatery that serves a variety of intergalactic taste treats catering to the visiting off-worlder.

The vast Vault of Haven is a holo-theater featuring the latest vids from the film capitols of the galaxy.

HALKAN

There are no mile high spires of admantium and steel or cities spanning whole continents on this planet. Instead the world offers a bucolic setting where visitors can commune with nature.

Halkans made technological advances to enhance the quality of life. There is no want, no ill health and no hunger.

The modest industrial society of Halkan is not a consumer culture. The Ferengi stopped visiting when they found that the Halkans had no interest in anything they had to offer. Ferengi complain they cannot trust people with no interest in Saurian Brandy.

The Halkans indulge in simple fare including dairy products and fish, but refuse to raise animals for slaughter. Their vast farmlands provide bounty for a vegetarian society. Food is grown naturally without radiation or chemicals.

People visit Organia to see super-aliens. Halkan holds no such attraction, only the opportunity to meet and talk with a people who have practiced peace for hundreds of years.

HAVEN

This idyllic planet in the Beta Cassius System is often chosen for marriage ceremonies. It offers large, groomed park lands close to cities with sky-spanning archways. Hotels feature wedding suites with domed ceilings clouded for privacy.

Visitors may rent solar powered aircars to circle the globe. The controls can be set to return the vehicles to their point of departure at any time. It is impossible to get lost.

The skies are filled with belts of carefully guided aerial traffic. No accidents have occurred in 25 years.

The best hotels are the Skyway Chapel, the Arch of Wonder and the Hilton Milespire, with the finest penthouse in the solar system.

Restaurants include the "Gakh of Glory," serving Klingon food prepared by four star Klingon chefs. Gakh is always served alive and squirming. "Saurian Andy" offers the off-world visitor a variety of intergalactic taste treats.

The Vault of Haven is a holo-theater showing the latest vids from the film capitols of the galaxy.

FOCUS On:

HOLBERG 917G: Holberg 917G is a shrine to Flint. He worked under various names, including Leonardo da Vinci, Johannes Brahms, and Galileo. A vast museum spanning three square miles has been erected. There is a combined hotel/restaurant complex on the top floor of the 20 story building. Although officially named the Galileo Gardens, some have nicknamed it the "Mona Leisure."

HOLBERG 917G

This gentle, blue, tropical world is a shrine to the memory of the man most recently known as "Flint." Born on Earth four thousand years ago, he began life in Mesopotamia as a man known as Akharin. He was a warrior who found he did not die when struck down in battle. He is Earth's first, and, perhaps, only, immortal.

Flint retired to this world. When he was discovered a century ago, he proved he had been Leonardo da Vinci, Johannes Brahms, Alexander the Great and Galileo. When he left Earth in the 23rd century, he began to age for the first time. He had lost his immortality by leaving the Earth, but he accepted this having grown weary of outliving those he loved.

Flint continued creating new works until his death. Today, a vast museum dedicated to his life spans three square miles, and includes a hotel/restaurant complex. Officially named the Galileo Gardens, it is as often called "Mona Leisure."

Many nations of Earth bid for the complex to be located in their own country, but it was decided that the planet Flint chose for his final home would be the ideal setting. This museum and monument commemorate his singular talents.

HOLBERG 917G

ICONIA

ICONIA

[See FORBIDDEN ZONES]

ICOR IX

One of the finest astrophysics centers in the Federation is located on this planet. It is the site of frequent symposiums.

This world has stable weather and a sky with some of the most interesting astronomical patterns in the galaxy. These include a black cluster and a spiral nebula that can be viewed at an angle perfect for holographic photography.

When the planetarium dome opens after sunset, a glittering expanse fills the heavens. Symposium discussions are held beneath this vault of night.

Icor Nine is an extraordinary world colonized by an astronomical society. The organization has an exclusive colony permit for this world.

The small planet is often called the "Forest World" because of the hundreds of thousands of square miles of virgin forest. There are no city lights to interfere with the work of seventy-seven active observatories. Underground habitats beneath the observatories provide living quarters.

Most visitors are astronomers, but zoologists fascinated by the ecosystem and wildlife on this world have also begun to arrive. A visa is required.

Arboria is a large hotel complex nestled in the forest kingdom. The owner is a fan of mid twentieth century Earth popular culture. This hotel is a village in the sky. Surrounded by treetops, the hotel doesn't interfere with their natural growth. Rooms with a leafy branch cost extra.

Icor IX offers many wonders for those interested in botany or astronomy. It is not a shore leave world, but a place to get away from it all and admire the wonders of unspoiled nature.

INDRI VIII

The atmosphere and ecosystem of this Class M planet were destroyed by a powerful plasma weapon. The Federation has refused to release the name or nationality of those responsible.

Since this was an uninhabited world the Prime Directive was not violated. The Federation has filed a formal protest and is seeking financial damages to clean up and terraform the world.

Until that happens, the planet is uninhabitable. Anyone wishing to buy the world willing to assume financial responsibility for terraforming is directed to contact Starfleet Command.

IOTIA

This may be the strangest planet in interplanetary tourism. It is occasionally dangerous but always amusing. The world's culture was forever altered by an unintentional violation of the Federation's Prime Directive.

A crewman aboard the USS Intrepid accidentally left behind a copy of the book, CHICAGO MOBS OF THE TWENTIES. This sensationalistic slice of Earth history impressed the Iotians. In one century, they built an entirely new tribal culture modeled on the warring gangs, forever redefining their "turf" and business interests.

This baffled the next starship crew to happen along. Fortunately, the resourceful captain found creative ways to work with the Iotians and set them on the path to unity. Unfortunately, the Iotians never quite reached the requisite one-world-government status required for Federation membership.

Iotians have an amazing ability to fragment just when things are going smoothly. They emulate any influence thrown their way, and have changed their society countless times. It's almost inevitable every time outsiders visit.

Tourists sometimes make this part of their itinerary. They want to see how much they can change the Iotian way of life in as short a time as possible. For this reason, pleasure trips to Iotia are discouraged by Federation authorities.

Trips are not illegal. The main barrier to tourism is the exorbitant price. Iotia is available only through Ferengi travel agents. The agents lure whimsical wealthy beings to Iotia with the promise that they can leave a lasting mark on the history and culture of the world.

What these unscrupulous Ferengi neglect to mention is that any change will last only until the next visitor catches Iotian fancy. Federation and Starfleet personnel regard assignment to Iotia as punitive.

FOCUS ON:

ICOR IX: A small planet often called the "Forest World" because of the hundreds of thousands of square miles of virgin woods. There are no city lights to interfere with 77 active observatories built across the planet.

Only two observatories, The Constellation and The Alien Touch, are open to tourism. They are connected to hotel complexes. The Alien Touch features a restaurant with a revolving menu of off-world dishes. Many off-world culinary delights are very seasonal. Some are only served at certain times of the year due to tradition or religious belief.

A vast hotel complex nestled in the forest kingdom has been named Arboria by its owner (a fan of mid-Twentieth Century Earth popular culture). The hotel is a village in the sky. It surrounds trees high above the ground without cutting into them or interfering with their natural growth. Rooms bisected by a leafy branch cost extra.

JANUS VI

This mineral rich world is of interest only to visiting mineralogists or specialists in xenobiology. The dark auburn color of the planet signals that it is no tropical paradise. The surface is bleak and rocky, virtually uninhabited except for a Federation landing base. The atmosphere is much too thin for humanoid life. A life support system is required.

The mining colony has been operational for 150 years. It has not exhausted the wealth of the world.

Miners have a symbiotic relationship with a strange creature known as the Horta. Native exclusively to Janus VI, the Horta lives in the rocks. It tunnels through them by exuding a powerful acid from its skin.

The miners were unaware of the Horta for fifty years. Then they stumbled onto the egg chamber (the "Chamber of the Ages") of the silicon based life form. The eggs looked like silicon nodules and were either broken or ignored in the search for the rich deposits of Pergium.

At the time, Pergium, a fissionable material, was a valuable power source. Substitutes have since been found.

Contact was established with the Horta and a cooperative arrangement was made. The Horta would tunnel where the miners instructed and its eggs and offspring would be left alone. Many other minerals were later discovered because of this arrangement.

FACTS TO TAKE INTO ACCOUNT The Horta is not intelligent enough to qualify for protection under the Prime Directive. Scientists study this unique life form. Cave explorers marvel at the tunnels made by the Horta.

Individual Horta have agreed to travel to other worlds to assist miners. Subsurface charts help direct the Horta's tunneling.

Janus VI is leased from the Federation under a one hundred year renewable contract. The contract requires that the Horta remain unmolested.

For decades the miners lived below the surface. Recently a domed village was constructed on the surface. It is used for extended R&R when the miners are allowed a month off following six months of subsurface work.

The dome is located in the northwestern quadrant. It is positioned so that the unusual atmospheric effects visible in the north, called the "Janus Lights," can be viewed. This effect appears to be a huge rainbow of light sweeping across the sky. A popular television show on Earth uses footage of this effect as part of its opening graphics.

Travel visas are not difficult to obtain, but they restrict tourists to areas not being mined. The dome is open to outside visitors. Tours of the surface, particularly of the caverns and tunnels below, are expensive.

Janus VI is most often visited by researchers. The Horta do run free. This world is not a zoo. The Horta secrete a solvent capable of melting rock and obliterating living tissue.

This unusual world is not a shore leave stopover.

⬡ *KAELON II*

Unusual cloud patterns obscure parts of the sky of this small, brownish-green world. Strange wind patterns in the upper atmosphere, blow them about.

Kaelon II is a member of the Federation. They do not break Federation laws by requiring suicide by all of their people as part of an elaborate ritual when they reach the age of 60. The "Age of Resolution" dates back hundreds of years to when Kaelon II was barely able to grow enough food to sustain itself.

When a famine struck, it was decided civilization could survive only by limiting life spans. Age 60 would be the limit. Beyond that age, a body grew infirm and became a drain on the community.

Eventually Kaelon II advanced and people remained strong and vital after the Age of Resolution. The law remained unchanged. It had become an honor to end one's life for the benefit of society.

Some fight to change this tradition. Most feel it is wrong to abandon a way handed down from their ancestors. Some support continuing the Age of Resolution because a person's estate is inherited sooner than if they lived out their normal life span.

This tradition of the world repels many outsiders and has garnered it the unofficial sobriquet, "Suicide world."

VISITORS TAKE NOTE If this custom ever changes it will be because so many off-worlders find it so offensive they refuse to set foot on Kaelon II. Some people mistaken-

---

FOCUS ON:

KLINZAI: Klingons are a lusty breed who enjoy food. Off-worlders often have difficulty developing a taste for the local delicacies.

The most well known is Gakh, which resembles a bowl of worms. This tasty treat is best served live. Serving half dead Gakh is considered very bad form. Klingons often serve dead Gakh to non-Klingons to test their knowledge of Klinzai. Chech'tluth is a Klingon alcoholic drink.

Klingon hotels are unique. One of the best is The War Room. It is a history museum of Klingon armaments. It is only a twenty story hotel but most major cities on Klinzai have a branch of this chain.

Another fine hotel is The Black Tower, a two hundred story structure built of a black metal. It has a fifty foot spire on the top to which an airboat is moored.

ly believe that if anyone over the age of 60 visits Kaelon II, they are subject to this ritual suicide. This, of course, is not true.

Some Kaelons do look oddly at the elderly who visit because there are no old people on this planet. It can make for uncomfortable moments when people are introduced.

Kaelon II has full weather control. Food production cannot be interrupted. The gross national product is more than the planet can use, creating a trade surplus. It is a thriving, modern world except for the oddity of the Age of Resolution.

KATAAN

A space probe launched from Kataan a thousand years ago was recently captured by a Federation starship. It is the only clue to the history of this world.

Today Kataan is a bleak, brownish-yellow planet covered with deserts and mountains. Underneath sit the remains of a long dead civilization.

A thousand years ago the system's star went nova and destroyed the culture just as the people began to discover the secrets of space flight. Unable to escape their world, they could only launch a satellite containing a chronicle their people. This chronicle reveals that the Kataan were simple, generous people who loved the arts and embraced science.

Today Kataan is a barren, empty world, standing as a memorial to the gentle people. The space probe preserved the music of Kataan. It contained one of their instruments, a Ressikan Flute. Visitors to Kataan study the history of this dead people and the relics found deep underground.

There are no hotels or ports of entry for tourists. Too much celebration seems inappropriate on this world that stands as a monument to a lost people.

KAVIS ALPHA SECTOR

A neutron star in this sector absorbs material from a red giant until it explodes every 196 years. It is rarely witnessed, although its most recent cycle was chronicled and recorded by a Federation starship.

There is a holo-logue of this event. Spectrometric readings can also be examined in detail.

Several worlds exist in this sector, including Kavis Alpha Four. A colony of nanites flourishes on this planet. Due to their ability to infect mechanical devices, it is not recommended that shuttles or vessels of any kind touch down on that world. While the nanites are not deliberately harmful, they expand into any available mechanical space.

KLINZAI

The Klingon homeworld is also referred to as Kling. Klinzai is completely paved over.

This world is ruled by a High Council. Gowron is the current leader, although a recent bloodless coup gave the long retired title of Emperor to Kahless. Rumor says

Kahless is the resurrection of the legendary warrior who lived fifteen hundred years ago. It is said that on Klinzai, anything is possible.

The Klingon/Federation peace accord signed seventy-five years ago opened this world to off-worlders. Few travelers respond to the invitation.

All Klingons are aggressive. To show weakness of any kind, even in simple conversation, is not the Klingon way.

Klingons venerate war. Their decision to sign an armistice with the Federation 75 years ago was a surprise. Not every everyone supported this peace accord. Factions on both sides opposed it and attempted to prevent it. The treaty has held and the Klingon Empire has remained an important ally of the Federation.

The Federation and the Klingon Empire almost engaged in war a century ago. This was prevented by the Organians who imposed a truce against the will of both parties. The Organians predicted that one day the Klingon Empire and the Federation would be allies. Neither side took this prophecy seriously at the time.

KLINGONESE CULTURE The Klingon culture is rich and complex, including many rites and rituals. These include the Age of Ascension and the Age of Inclusion, both critical in the passage of the Klingon male to adulthood.

The Age Of Ascension requires a Klingon's friends to beat him with pain sticks. This rite of passage is repeated on certain anniversaries.

The ritual of the Majqa involves going into a trance state to see visions and seek revelations about one's deceased father. Patriarchy is very strong in Klingon culture.

Discommendation is the Klingon ritual of disgrace when an individual is cast from the Klingon empire and stripped of all rights and property. Discommendation results from an act of disgrace by the individual or someone in his family that brings disgrace on the entire family line.

The person is placed on trial in the "Mek'ba." The Klingon legal system includes a defender called a cha'Dlch. A cha'Dlch is appointed to defend the accused.

Honor is paramount to Klingons. To question a Klingon's honor can result in an immediate duel to the death. The greatest honor for a Klingon is to die in battle.

The greatest disgrace a Klingon can experience is to be captured in battle and imprisoned. A Klingon would sooner remain in prison than be released to return home and have his entire family disgraced. Captured Klingons often attack their guards hoping to be killed rather than face the ignominy of imprisonment like an animal in a cage.

Family is important to Klingons. The Jinag is the name of an amulet given to a daughter when she comes of age.

WARRIOR RITUALS Weapons are an important part of Klingon heritage. The Gin'tak spear is an ancient weapon now used in ceremonies and personal battles. Qa'vak is a type of target practice employing the Gin'tak.

The Kut'luch is a weapon of assassination.

A ritual called a "Klingon Tea Ceremony" involves a vile drink toxic to humans unless an antidote is consumed in advance. Klingons relish the drink.

KLINZAI

The most frightening ritual is the Klingon Death Chant. A warrior stands over the body of a fallen Klingon and howls out a warning at the top of his lungs that a Klingon is on his way to the nether world. It is as close to a religious belief as Klingon culture embraces, other than the worship of the memory of fallen heroes.

Klingons believe in life after death. This is called "Sto-Vo-Kor."

THE LEGEND OF KAHLESS Kahless has become a legendary figure of great importance to Klingons. The world of Boreth is the central place for study and worship of this Klingon warrior who lived and fought 1500 years ago.

One revered artifact is the knife of Kirom, said to be stained with the blood of Kahless.

The High Clerics predicted his return. These Guardians of Boreth verified the miraculous re-appearance of the legendary Kahless.

Part of the legend tells of the forging of the bat'leth sword, a story known only to the High Clerics of Boreth. The man calling himself Kahless knew this story. That confirmed he is the genuine Kahless.

The Federation prefers not to get involved in religious matters as long as Federation laws are not violated. The Federation has remained silent as to the reappearance of Kahless. It is clear the Klingons believe the claim and the man was named Emperor, the moral and spiritual guardian of the Klingon people.

FACTS TO TAKE INTO ACCOUNT The "R'uusta," also known as "The Bonding," involves the creation of ties of kinship and brotherhood between two people not blood relations. It is sometimes used when one person adopts another as part of his family.

Less dramatic is the "Mok'Bara," a Klingon exercise ritual. This routine helps center the mind and body and is practiced during times of great stress.

Recent notable Klingons include Kor, Koloth and Kang. All still lived until recently. Kang and Koloth were slain in a campaign to avenge the death of their sons 81 years ago. Only Kor remained to sound the death chant for his slain comrades.

Travelers visiting this planet should read the COMPLETE KLINGON CULTURE INDEX, a thorough listing of all known Klingon cultural practices.

A popular book on Klinzai is DREAM OF FIRE, written by a Terran. Its Klingon translation has become a bestseller. While some books lose something in the translation, this one apparently gained during the transposition.

Klingons are a lusty breed who enjoy their food. Off-worlders may have to work at acquiring a taste for local delicacies. The best known is Gakh, which resembles a bowl of worms. It is best served live. Serving half dead Gakh is very bad form, but Klingons often try this to see how much non-Klingons know about the food and culture of Klinzai.

Less demanding is Chech'tluth, an Klingon alcoholic drink.

CLOAKED IN HISTORY A common piece of Klingon technology, the cloaking device, enables a vessel to be invisible to both sight and sensors. The Romulans may have developed the technology and sold it to the Klingons a century ago or Klingons may have invented it. The peace accords with the Klingon Empire uphold a treaty the Federation has with the Romulans against developing similar technology.

The Federation may borrow Klingon vessels, but the cloaking technology may not be installed on non-Klingon ships. This treaty with the Romulans has prevented war for two hundred years, despite difficult relations in recent years.

Klingons don't like Romulans. They have made it clear that should the Romulans ever threaten them as they did Vulcan, all out war will result. The Klingons enjoy fighting even more than Romulans do.

RECOMMENDATIONS FOR TRAVELERS One of the best Klingon hotels is The War Room, which features a museum of armaments from Klingon conflicts going back 500 years. This twenty story hotel is part of a chain with locations in most major cities on Klinzai.

Another fine hotel is The Black Tower, a two hundred story structure. It is built of a black metal with a fifty foot spire on the top to which a single airboat is moored. Each day a lone Klingon warrior scales the outside of the building until he reaches the spire and climbs into the airboat to return to the ground. Climbers refuse to wear antigrav safety vests. Klingons do not fear death when it results from an act of bravery.

The Qa'vak hotel has an adjoining amphitheater in which teams of Klingons hold violent contests involving pain sticks and other ritual devices. It is not a disgrace for a Klingon to lose these contests as long as he breaks a bone or suffers a gruesome injury. Any other way wouldn't be Klingon.

◉ KOINONIA

On this planet hundreds of years ago, two civilizations destroyed each other in war. Only the invisible, disembodied Koinonian race still exists. These powerful non-corporeal entities are not threatening. They respond to strong emotions and try to remedy problems when other races contact them, however inadvertent that contact may be.

The ruins of Koinonian civilization still exist. A recent Starfleet survey team accidentally discovered active Koinonian mines, subspace proximity detectors, when one exploded and killed a member of an away team. The remaining Koinonians found, dug up and defused the other five mines to insure that such a tragic accident could never take place again.

Starfleet has confirmed that there are no more mines. Walking the wide thoroughfares, a visitor wonders at the fury of the conflict that caused skyscrapers to melt and streets to flow with molten stone. Skeletons of structures lie bent and twisted like giants painfully struck down by mammoth warriors. The world remains a monument to the destructive power of modern warfare.

Today many Federation schools show holo-views of this world with the visible scars of violent, all-consuming warfare. Visitors are permitted.

⊜ *LIGON II*

This world is not a member of the Federation. Negotiations have been going on for several years.

Initial contact proved problematical when the leader of the planet kidnapped a Starfleet officer he wanted to make his wife. He was quite annoyed when the Federation complained. The Ligonese believe their customs should apply to all visitors.

Personal rights and individual liberty clash with basic tenets of Ligon law. Some refer to the peculiar customs on this world as "Ligon Lingo."

The leader of Ligon II is the Primary; his vast estate is the "Centerplace." This home is given to the new Primary when the old one is supplanted.

The main wife of the Primary is The First One. Men on Ligon II have many wives. A wife is freed from her marriage bond only by death.

When the Primary's First One died during battle with the kidnapped Starfleet officer and was then revived, this satisfied the letter of the law. She dissolved her marriage to the Primary. Since women own property on Ligon II, The Primary found himself disinherited.

The people of Ligon are aggressive but lack the technology to pose a threat to neighboring worlds. The Federation hopes to tame them because Ligon II could gain much from commerce with the Federation.

Visitors are allowed on Ligon II. The appropriate chapter of THE HITCHHIKER'S GUIDE TO THE GALAXY reveals the pitfalls for the tourist hoping to deal with Ligonese.

There are no hotels, only primitive inns. Basic Federation credits are grudgingly accepted at an exorbitant exchange rate.

⊙ MALKIS IX

Temperatures vary from continent to continent on this class M world. Winters are harsher than on Earth, but summers are mild. There are vast mountain ranges, salt oceans and dune deserts.

The planet is home to the Lairons, a humanoid species famous for developing writing before speech or sign language. It is renowned for cultural centers, museums, literature, plays and dramas.

The theatre of Malkis IX is popular with most humanoid species. The Federation Tourist Board recommends booking tickets far in advance.

RECOMMENDATIONS FOR TRAVELERS Lairons suffer little disease, but inoculations are required before visiting.

Malkis IX has a variety of insects. Natives are immune to most of their bites and stings, but off-worlders must be protected.

Malkis is home to the giant furry lion-spider that can grow to four feet in length. The Lairons have domesticated them and keep them as pets. They are docile and affectionate and never bite unless provoked.

Lion-spiders spin webs of the softest silk. Lairons make clothing from these webs.

Another interesting species is the balloon-beetle, which can grow to six feet in length and four feet tall. They float on helium bladders. They are harmless herbivores.

Animal life is bountiful. Camera safaris are popular with visitors.

FOCUS ON:

MARS: Hotels are centered in the northern hemisphere cities of Bradbury and Burroughs. Museums memorialize these authors who wrote extensively about the red planet, although their fiction strayed far from Martian reality. Recommended hotels include the Martian Clientele and the Helium Towers.

Clouds of water ice trail from the giant volcano Ascraeus Mons. This wonder can be seen from orbit. Olympus Mons is the largest of the Martian volcanoes, 375 miles across at its base and fifteen miles high. Its crater is 40 miles wide. Many a traveler has attempted to scale its peak but none have succeeded in reaching the top.

Valles Marineris is a large series of valleys stretching for three thousand miles and up to 50 miles across with cliffs up to five miles high. The crater Argyre is a favorite spot to photograph and explore.

Because a vacant Mars was colonized by Earth, there is no native food.

FACTS TO TAKE INTO ACCOUNT Lairons are peaceful, friendly people. It is smart to review their laws before visiting. A copy of planetary laws is available from the Federation Tourist Bureau on request.

Gambling, smoking and yelling in public enact high fines. Hunting is illegal.

Many resorts cater to discriminating tastes. Mountain ski resorts offer year-round service. Beach resorts in more temperate zones allow year-round swimming, though humans should be warned temperatures are cooler than Earth norm.

There are resorts on the three moons, Wintere, Phyre and Lathe. Gambling is legal on these moons. They offer an adult atmosphere.

Resorts accommodate non-humanoid species, but it is best to check before making reservations. The Lairons take all Federation currencies and credit cards.

 **MALKOR**

[See FORBIDDEN WORLDS]

MALURIAN SYSTEM

Do not visit!

This system was destroyed 75 years ago in a freak accident. A machine programmed to destroy inferior carbon-based infestations killed the four billion intelligent people in the system. Nothing remained for salvage.

The planets were Maluria I, II, III and IV. The sun, Omega Cygni, now shines only on the remains of the four worlds. Expensive shuttle tours take historians and scientists around the site.

Not recommended.

MANARK IV

This is a class M world of rock and sand with small salt oceans. The land mass is denser than that of Earth. Wildlife is abundant. There is no intelligent life.

RECOMMENDATIONS FOR TRAVELERS Tourists brave this world in protected vehicles. The wildlife is dangerous; precautions must be taken.

Most dangerous is the sandbat. Sandbats range in size from six inches to ten feet in length. Their wingspans can range up to thirty feet.

The sandbat can blend into this rocky world and fool its prey. When the sandbat's unsuspecting prey approaches, the sandbat attacks. Their bite is deadly to humanoid beings and many non-humanoid species. The poison takes effect almost immediately. There is an antidote. All visitors are advised to carry this antidote at all times.

The antidote is effective only if administered within twelve minutes of being bitten. The victim should then immediately be warped to the nearest hospital.

Other interesting wildlife includes the prickly cat. Its coat of spines can shoot as far as ten feet to pierce its victims. The four to six foot amphibious salamander shark lives in the ocean and on shore and attacks whatever moves across its line of vision. The deadly boa bush looks like a snake but is a form of plant life that subsists on the blood of its victims after it has squeezed them to death.

FACTS TO TAKE INTO ACCOUNT There are no resorts on Manark IV. The world is a complete wilderness. Campers must remain within their vehicles.

Combination shuttle/campers can be rented from a nearby orbiting space station, Deep Space 3. All persons wishing to visit this world must sign in with the Manark rangers on Deep Space 3. If the camper does not return by the expected date, a search party will be organized.

This is a hostile environment recommended only for experienced campers and shuttle pilots.

Hunting is strictly forbidden. Manark's wildlife is protected. High penalties and fines are levied if wildlife is harmed, even in self-defense.

Do not put yourself at risk. Stay in your campers with defense shields up at all times. Make sure you have sufficient supplies if you get stuck and have to wait for rescue.

Deep Space 3's shuttle/camper rental companies are mostly Ferengi run. They prefer to deal strictly in gold press latinum. However, most galactic credit cards are also accepted with a hefty surcharge added.

 MARS

Mars is the fourth planet of the Sol System. The system is home to the capitol of the United Federation of Planets, Earth.

Mars was a dead planet until it was colonized by Earth settlers in the late 21st century. It is plagued by rough weather and high winds that blow deadly dust storms.

Martians live in tightly secured and sealed domed biospheres. There are orbital colonies of Mars referred to as Martian Colonies.

RECOMMENDATIONS FOR TRAVELERS The Utopia Planitia Shipyards, named after a northern plain of Mars, orbit the planet. They are famous throughout the galaxy for constructing amazing starships of great size and strength. Daily tours of these shipyards are educational and exciting for visitors.

Mars can be scouted by short range shuttle or vehicles specially built to withstand the terrain. The thin atmosphere cannot support humanoid life. It is 90 percent carbon dioxide with small amounts of nitrogen and argon and traces of carbon monoxide, oxygen and water vapor. Suits are required.

Martian volcanoes are beautiful to behold. Plumes of clouds containing water ice trail from the giant volcano Ascraeus Mons. This wonder can be seen from orbit.

Olympus Mons is the largest of the Martian volcanoes, 375 miles across at its base and fifteen miles high. Its crater is 40 miles wide. Many a well-suited traveler has attempted to climb its peaks but none have succeeded in reaching the top.

Valles Marineris is a large series of valleys stretching for three thousand miles, and up to 50 miles across. Some cliffs are five miles high from the floor of the valleys.

The crater Argyre is also a favorite spot to photograph and explore.

FACTS TO TAKE INTO ACCOUNT Temperatures on Mars range from a high of 30 C (80 F) to a low of -125 C (-190 F). Mars has seasons. The Martian year lasts 780 Earth days, or two Earth years and two months.

Mars has two moons, Phobos and Deimos, which support no life. The moons are asteroids pulled into Mars' orbit.

Polar caps are covered with "dry ice," frozen carbon dioxide, with water ice underneath. The dust on Mars consists of iron oxides. Its reddish color gives the world its popular name, "the red planet."

Mars is a very rocky planet with many valleys, mountains and plains. It is a beautiful place to visit, and much geological information has been learned from this small, dead world.

MELKOT

Hotels are centered in the northern hemisphere cities of Bradbury and Burroughs. Museums memorialize these two authors who both wrote extensively about the red planet. Although their fiction strayed far from Martian reality, the authors captured the popular imagination. Their stories are believed to have fueled interest in colonizing Earth's nearest neighbor.

 **MELKOT**

This world is the home of the Melkots, or 'Melkotians,' as humanoid species refer to them. It is ringed with 'no trespassing' signs. Warning buoys advise travelers to steer clear.

Melkots do not like unannounced visitors. They might welcome you with open arms or an illusion to test your worthiness. If you fail, you might be killed.

Melkots judge others by their own standards. They believe in strict non-violence, but use illusional violence to stop others. They have no patience with conflict and do not belong to the Federation.

FOCUS ON:

MALKIS IX: This world is renowned for cultural centers and museums. Their writers enchant hundreds of worlds. Their dramatic theatre is popular with most humanoid species. The Federation Tourist Board recommends getting tickets far in advance.

The world offers resorts for a variety of tastes. Mountain ski resorts, such as the Himalaya Hilton, offer year-round service. Beach resorts set in temperate zones allow year-round swimming, though humans should be warned that temperatures are cooler than Earth norm.

The Hot Tropic offers weather control in the immediate vicinity of the hotel. This boosts the ambient temperature for a full mile radius (sometimes causing strange weather a hundred miles away by creating unusual high pressure zones). The resorts also accommodate non-humanoid species but check into the specifics before making your reservations.

There are also resorts on the three moons, Wintere, Phyre and Lathe. Since these resorts are technically off-world, gambling is legal. They offer an adult atmosphere. The Lairons take all Federation currency and credit cards.

They are a solitary race. In the last 70 years, they have begun negotiating trade agreements. They now allow a few chosen students, artists and parapsychologists to tour their world.

RECOMMENDATIONS FOR TRAVELERS Melkot is a highly advanced world, with crystal cities and clear, fresh water seas. The air is sweet and clean.

Melkots pride themselves on intellectual and psychic pursuits. Vulcans and Betazoids interest them, and they are hungry for knowledge of the outside universe attained by Federation exploration starships.

FACTS TO TAKE INTO ACCOUNT Melkots have advanced robots with sophisticated artificial intelligence to tend their cities and homes, build, and even create art.

Efficient robots led the Melkots to become less social and more introverted and paranoid. They 'live in their minds' most of the time.

Melkots are solitary beings who prefer to live alone and mate only to have children. Little is known of their mating habits. Their biology, and even gender, remains a mystery.

Children are raised by robot parents and attendants and grow up to live lives apart. When Melkots meet outsiders, or even each other, they often use robot facsimiles.

The real Melkot operates the facsimile from the safety of his own home. Melkots do not want uninvited outsiders visiting their world.

If you apply for a visa and are chosen, the Melkots will be gracious hosts offering first class accommodations at no cost. Melkots earn no money from tourism. No money or credit cards are accepted. All needs of the approved visitor are met for free.

Offering a Melkot monetary payment for hospitality is an insult. Your trip will be cut short.

⊚ MEMORY ALPHA

The small planetoid houses the central information archive of the United Federation of Planets. It stores the accumulated sum of all known information about the galaxy.

The complete historical data of every Federation member world is stored here, as is all available information about the histories, cultures and science of all other planets, living or dead. Scientific knowledge, ranging from biology to archaeology, from subdimensional physics to infrastellar dynamics, can be accessed by anyone.

Memory Alpha is dedicated to the freedom of information. Some classified Starfleet data may be excluded.

This site was severely damaged in its early years a century ago. It was extensively rebuilt and has operated without incident since.

Not everyone's idea of a resort, but for information junkies this is nirvana. Limited facilities are available for visitors. Memory Alpha includes an amphitheater and fifty individual vid cubicles. All films in Memory Alpha can also be accessed from orbiting ships.

⊚ MERAK II

This class M world is a botanist's paradise. Scientists from all over the galaxy come to study.

This is a warm, humid world. Winters are almost non-existent, except at the poles.

This lush, green world was once threatened by a disease that killed all the plant life. The plants recovered after being treated with zienite. Zienite mined on the world of Ardana is still used to protect the plant life of Merak II. The non-human inhabitants encourage a tourist trade to pay for the zienite.

RECOMMENDATIONS FOR TRAVELERS Tree house resorts run by the Merakites are popular vacation spots for travelers of all races and species. Sights not to miss include Tree City, which offers the finest in shopping, restaurants and entertainment.

Frozen deserts attract many visitors every year. Beaches are large and clean.

The only hazard to swimmers is from the seaweed monster. The plant draws its prey underwater by tangling it in vines, then feeds off the slowly decaying body tissues through its porous membranes. The seaweed monster is carefully controlled by expert Merakites, who periodically thin the herds and keep them well-fed and away from shallower waters. In the last century, no seaweed monster has been known to attack visiting or native swimmers at the designated, safe beaches.

FACTS TO TAKE INTO ACCOUNT The DNA of Merakites is plant-based. They are related to plants, and able to read their auras.

Merakites are thin, leafy, green beings with stem-like bodies. Their culture is based on reverence for plants as intelligent beings. Oddly, they are also vegetarians, thus technically cannibals.

Tours are offered of their special farms, where they grow food and other products. This planet is also home to the gatherer bee, an insect responsible for ninety percent of plant pollination. The gatherer bee plays a role in the reproductive process of the Merakites.

It is a highly revered insect. Cults and religions have been developed around this insect. Without the gatherer bee, the Merakites would be extinct.

The bee is the symbol on their planetary flag. It does not sting, and is friendly in nature. Merakites have domesticated the gatherer bee over the last few thousand years.

The bee ranges in size from one inch to five inches in length. They ignore visitors and remain close to Merakites or other plant life. They are very territorial and very shy.

The annual festival of the gatherer bee resembles a Mardi Gras. It is a week long celebration that occurs at the height of the tourist season. It is usually held in the summer of Merak's southern hemisphere.

Merak II is a Federation world and takes all known Federation currencies and credit. Primary hotels include the Holiday Inn Marak, The Galactic Hive and the aforementioned Inn of Tree City.

MIDOS V

This heavily populated world is home to colonists of more than twenty different worlds and species. Residents include human, Andorian, Tellarite, Deltan, Betazoid, Vulcan, Merakite, Kelvan, Rigellian, Ardanan, Klingon, Argelian, Bajoran, Ferengi and many other humanoid and non-humanoid beings. They believe the original Vulcan philosophy of Infinite Diversity in Infinite Combinations. Interracial adoption and marriages are encouraged.

This world is home to the famous Unified Galactic Front. Their aim is peace in the galaxy for all species living as one big family. Dissenters fear dissolution of valuable cultural influences that separatism keeps alive, but the Midosians believe culture can be kept alive through education and records. They have a vast archival central complex that preserves hundreds of histories of different races throughout the known galaxy.

RECOMMENDATIONS FOR TRAVELERS Midos offers a great variety of things to do for visitors of all races. The Class M world offers oceans, deserts, forests, plains, tundra and mountains to explore. Though the planet is heavily populated, there are still large unexplored territories for the adventurous traveler.

Cities are hospitable. Elaborate quarters provide for non-air breathers.

Midos is famous for its cultural centers and libraries. Scholars come to conduct research because, except for Memory Alpha, this world's libraries are the most diverse and complete in the known galaxy.

Weather is close to Earth norm.

FACTS TO TAKE INTO ACCOUNT Native Midosians are humanoid but, for reasons unknown to outsiders, rarely mate. Their race was dying out. They encouraged alien colonists to come to their world to increase its population and diversify its culture.

There are only a few dozen remaining native Midosians. None have offspring. Scientists study this phenomenon, but the Midosians seem unconcerned. They are content their world will live on, their culture preserved in vast, planetary archives.

This Federation world takes currency in all known Federation forms, and that of non-Federation worlds. There is a very advanced banking network and contact with hundreds of worlds. Much income comes from banking and investments on many different worlds. The prime lending rate is the lowest in the galaxy o encourage further immigration.

Unemployment is high. This is an inexpensive world for tourists to visit.

Venara is an ocean resort in the mid-continent. The best winter resort is Mordon, located in the Ardak Mountains along the 38th parallel. Resort rates are cheap, and travel arrangements can even be made through the Midosian government for rock bottom rates.

 **minara**

A planetary system's sun went nova in the mid-23rd century. The inhabitants of one world were saved by the help of a race of beings known as the Vians.

The Vians knew they could only save and relocate one race. The Minaran empaths were chosen. They were relocated to a world on the far edge of Federation territory. The new world was renamed Minara by the Vians.

This new world was banned to tourists for nearly 75 years as the empaths resettled on their new planet. It has now opened to trade and the possibility of becoming a member of the Federation.

FACTS TO TAKE INTO ACCOUNT The empaths of Minara are mutes who communicate primarily through sign language. They are not deaf, but can hear and understand Galactic Standard.

Their hospitals are rapidly gaining fame throughout the galaxy since Minaran empaths are natural healers. Healing is traumatic and personal for both healer and patient. Further research is being conducted to ease the burden on the healer.

The hospitals of Minara are not open to the general public outside Minara except in extreme emergencies. The empaths are a peaceful people with a history remarkably free of war.

In the past, they were solitary people with little real community. This was probably a self-defense mechanism due to their empathy for each other's pain.

Lack of verbal speech may have played a role in their isolation from each other. They have evolved into a brilliant species with communities that welcome outsiders.

RECOMMENDATIONS TO TRAVELERS Minara's temperatures are Earth-like, cold in the winters, warm in the summers. The world offers tropical beaches and giant wild forests untouched by civilization.

Exploration of these frontiers is encouraged by the empaths. Hunting and littering carry heavy penalties.

Resorts are proliferating on this new world. Tourism is becoming big business.

The empaths trade in their own, native currency, but resorts can take Federation credit. Gambling is illegal at this time. Selected areas may open for gambling soon.

Minara offers great skiing, hiking and swimming resorts on the principal continent of Onat. The cities of Brel, Hydyn and Burratok all have fine hotels with competitive rates. Transportation is by shuttle car, which can be rented for a nominal fee. A shuttle license is required. A licensed pilot can be hired.

 MINOS

[See FORBIDDEN WORLDS]

MINOS KOVA

This Federation world on the edge of Cardassian space acts as an outpost for the Federation. It supports a heavy Starfleet population.

The rugged, mountainous world has vast oceans subject to heavy, unpredictable storms. Weather control is not yet operational. This is still a wild world at this time.

A large mining corporation, Childress and Daughters, Inc., employs most of the population.

RECOMMENDATIONS FOR TRAVELERS Temperatures on this world are unpredictable. They range from below freezing to as high as 120 Fahrenheit on a given day. Seasons are unpredictable. Winters can be hot, summers cold. Remember to pack accordingly.

This world is now free of virus and disease, but it's still a good idea to make sure you are current on all inoculations, especially if you are humanoid.

Accommodations on Minos Kova provide living facilities for both human and non-humanoid species. There are all kinds of adult entertainments set up by the miners in league with Ferengi investors.

Resorts offer gambling, live theatre and the latest in galactic tri-d entertainment. This planet has two special theme amusement parks, one in the southern hemisphere, one in the northern. They are Ferengi run and are not located on Starfleet owned property.

FACTS TO TAKE INTO ACCOUNT Minos Kova was once home to a race of beings known as Kovatians. They long ago abandoned their world, leaving behind cities but few clues as to where they went.

Legends say the Kovatians discovered doorways to other dimensions. These doorways are said to appear and disappear at random. The Kovatians supposedly learned to control the doorways.

Evidence seems to confirm that all Kovatians on Minos Kova disappeared within a short time several millenniums ago. Kovatian writings tell of the dimensional doorways.

Speculation is that the Minos Kovatians are safe and well, having left this dimension for one that better suited them.

Reports of unexplained parapsychological activity are prevalent on this world, including sightings of ghostly beings, objects moving by themselves and other poltergeist activity. Starfleet has taken note of this and is studying the matter.

The events seem harmless and do not interfere with regular Starfleet routines. The miners also seem unconcerned with the strange happenings.

Residents become accustomed to unexplained phenomena. Psychically sensitive species should be forewarned. Visiting this world might affect you more strongly than psi-null species. Parapsychological activity could influence your dream-state as well as your waking state. However, if you are used to such things, or can shield at will, the activity should cause few problems.

 MIRI

This class M world suffered a great tragedy almost four centuries ago. Its entire adult population was wiped out by a virus constructed to prolong life. Instead, all adults died and life was prolonged only in prepubescent children, allowing them to age one month for every one hundred years.

The children called themselves 'Onlies' since they were the 'only' survivors. They were not discovered until three hundred years after the adults died. The starship Enterprise, then commanded by Captain James T. Kirk, discovered this planet.

FOCUS ON:

MERAK II: Primary hotels include the Holiday Inn Marak, The Galactic Hive and the Inn of Tree City. The tree house resorts, run by the Merakites, are popular vacation spots for travelers of all races and species. Other sights worth visiting include Tree City, which offers the finest in shopping, restaurants and entertainment.

This world is lush, warm and humid. Winters are very short, except at the famous polar frozen deserts.

The large beaches are very clean. The seaweed monster is hazardous to swimmers. The plant tangles its prey in vines, then slowly absorbs the decaying body through its porous membranes. No seaweed monster has been known to attack swimmers who stick to designated, safe beaches. Wild beaches are not recommended to swimmers.

Merak II is a Federation world. It accepts all known Federation currency and credit.

The children ran wild in the ruins of one of Miri's smaller cities, living off canned foods ransacked from stores and warehouses. When a child entered puberty, they caught the virus and died. The Enterprise crew discovered the children in this hellish atmosphere.

Before the crew succumbed to the virus, they invented an antidote. Later, other child survivors were found in other cities on all continents. Starfleet political and alien cultural affairs officers helped the children put their nearly dead civilization back together.

FACTS TO TAKE INTO ACCOUNT Miri is named after one of the eldest girls, thirteen when the disease hit, and thus 313 when encountered. This girl was instrumental in helping Starfleet officers rescue the children from the hideous life-prolongation plague.

Miri is still a prime influence in the planet's ongoing healing process. At a healthy 388 years old, she holds the office of Prime Minister. The cities have been rebuilt, and humanoid immigrants welcomed.

Mirians are completely human in appearance. Their planet is a near parallel to Earth, with almost exactly the same ratios of land to seas.

Miri has beautiful beaches and mountain ranges, wilderness forest areas and deserts. They are an official Federation world, and allow Federation citizens to immigrate, work and trade.

Resorts have been built to encourage tourism. The largest and most popular is called "Grup," after the slang word the children used for adults.

This world offers everything Earth has to offer, but with a much younger, less technological flair. The cities are smaller, the population less. Miri remains peaceful and beautiful, a parallel Earth untouched by the more modern events.

Gambling is legal on Miri. Some resorts are home to giant amusement parks to lure tourists, and offer entertainments of all varieties. Miri has a tragic history, but the survivors rebuilt a veritable paradise. Visit here today, and see for yourself.

⊚*MIZAR II*

This class M world is home to the Mizarians, a nonviolent race who never engage in war. They have been conquered six times in the last 300 years.

Mizarians hold great respect for outsiders. They are shy after being repeatedly conquered.

This planet offers beautiful seas and forests for tourists to explore. Mizarians are friendly to outsiders, accepting all forms of currency in trade, and insisting only that visitors bring no weapons. Hunting is forbidden.

RECOMMENDATIONS FOR TRAVELERS The Mizarian Temples For Peace, vast, multi-corridored complexes housing libraries, archives and research laboratories, preserve the knowledge of the Mizarians. Mizarians never raise a hand in conflict. Instead they devote time and energy to preserving the wisdom of the ages.

The Temples are open for tours. The architecture of these Temples is amazing. It is currently being studied by Federation apprentice architects. Mizar also has good ski resorts and beach resorts. They cater to humanoid species only.

⊚*MOAB IV*

This desolate world houses an enclosed, dome society known as a Genome colony. The inhabitants are highly advanced humans with technological capabilities equal to those of the Federation. Moabians value art and science.

The colony was discovered by the Enterprise under the command of Captain Jean-Luc Picard. A stellar core fragment was causing massive earthquakes on Moab IV. The colony was in jeopardy. Although the closed society wanted no outside contact, the Enterprise helped them survive the disruption of their world.

This contact revealed to the inhabitants that an entire civilization lived beyond the stars. The immigrant colony from Earth had been founded before the massive Galactic Expansion. Once the inhabitants learned of the changes beyond their sphere, many wanted to emigrate off-world.

The closed, balanced society quickly became unbalanced. Interference by the Enterprise saved their lives but destroyed their way of life.

RECOMMENDATIONS FOR TRAVELERS Moab IV is no longer a closed colony. To survive, it remains in contact with Starfleet and the Federation. It now allows outside trade and immigration to maintain its biosphere.

The colony can only support a limited number of people. Visitors must place their names on waiting lists and wait to be chosen to visit the biosphere. Immigrants are wanted, but screening is rigid. Once on the planet, treatment is first class.

Moab is an untouched paradise. The people are peaceful and happy. Music festivals are an almost daily occurrence in Moab's parks. Children are welcome. Recreation includes swimming, live theatre, concerts and two museums devoted to Moabian culture.

Moab is a year-round, sedate 72 F to 78 F. The Moabian colony currently only supports humanoid life. Non-humanoids must make special arrangements in advance, and may not be able to visit.

Visitors remember the world's highly advanced dome. Hikes to the edge of the dome to view the desolate, rocky world are popular. One side of the glass is a virtual paradise in perpetual spring, the other a dead, airless badlands of supercooled rock with jagged cliffs and crumbled valleys.

The leader of Moab IV, Aaron Conor, has held office for over a decade. He first opposed tourism, then changed his mind for the good of the colony.

 M113

This desert world supports humanoid life. It once housed a creature now known as the Salt-Vampire. The Salt-Vampire became completely extinct a century ago.

The last one was discovered by archeologists Robert and Nancy Crater. The creature could change shape into human or other forms. It killed Nancy Crater because of its desperate hunger for salt.

The Enterprise, under command of Captain James T. Kirk, destroyed the creature in self-defense. Though preserving the creature would have been the best option, logs indicate the creature could not be safely secured. It was a danger to all who met it. Its hypnotic talents, ability to shape shift and primitive desire to feed at any cost simply made it too dangerous.

RECOMMENDATIONS TO TRAVELERS M113 is an archeologist's delight. Ancient ruins holding the secrets of the race that once inhabited this world are scattered across the planet.

There is only sporadic plant-life on this world. Vicious winds suddenly sweep the planet. This hasn't stopped scientists from combing this world end to end.

Elaborate museums house what they have found. They are dedicated to M113's past civilization and natural history. Small 'pioneer' towns have sprung up to house the scientists, but there are no formal tourist resorts or vacation spots.

M113

This rural world is for those who like primitive nature and scouting out ruins of lost civilizations. Camping is encouraged. All water must be brought. Strict laws forbid removing contents from the ruins or taking plant-life. This world is a protected Federation park. Scientists studying the planet have special permits to remove artifacts from their natural resting spots.

THE MYSTERY OF M113 No one knows what caused the extinction of this civilization. The journals of Professor and Nancy Crater tell of the remaining Salt-Vampire and how its kind was hunted to extinction. This information came from the Salt-Vampire, and is highly suspect.

Scientists believe the Salt-Vampire ran out of its natural prey and turned on the natives of M113, hunting them to extinction. When all animal life was gone, the Salt-Vampires turned on each other until only one left.

The Salt-Vampire can change shape. It would be nearly impossible for an intelligent species to defend itself against this ability. An entire civilization could be destroyed by such a monster.

Maverick theorists speculate that M113 may not be the natural habitat of the Salt-Vampire. The theorists propose that the vampires came from another world. Their arrival resulted in the destruction of all life on the new world. The original home of the Salt-Vampires has never been established.

⊚ M-33 GALAXY

This is not a good place to visit at this time. It is located nearly three million light years from our Milky Way Galaxy.

This galaxy has, in theory, only been visited by beings who can travel outside time, such as the Travelers. The starship Enterprise, captained by Jean-Luc Picard, was accidentally brought to this galaxy by a Traveler.

Little is known about this galaxy. Travel to it would take millennia without the help of a Traveler.

The Federation has no way to contact the Travelers. It is believed the Travelers would refuse to help such trips unless they picked the voyagers. Little is known about the Travelers. They appear only to choose people for purposes not publicly shared.

FOCUS ON:

MIRI: Cities are small and population is low, so Miri remains peaceful and beautiful, almost a parallel Earth untouched by the events that make Earth crowded and busy.

Miri may have a tragic history, but the survivors have rebuilt their world into a veritable paradise. Gambling is legal. Some resorts house giant amusement parks to lure tourists with entertainment of all varieties. The largest and most popular is called "Grup," named after the slang word the children used to describe adults.

The only others who may know the way are the seemingly omniscient Q species from the Q Continuum. They have never been cooperative in sharing useful information. The reclusive Q have motives few in the Federation understand.

The M-33 Galaxy is not a good vacation prospect for the near future.

⊚ MUDD'S PLANET

This is a world of underground labyrinths and chambers with artificially induced class M conditions. It is home to a race of androids created by an extinct, advanced race from the Andromeda Galaxy.

This world was an outpost of that extinct race, referred to by the androids as the Makers. The androids are all that remain of that advanced Andromedan civilization.

Mudd's Planet was named after the rapscallion rogue of Federation lore known as Harcourt Fenton Mudd, a felon wanted for crimes on more than fourteen known worlds in the Federation. His ship crash-landed on the world, and the androids saved his life, then kept him prisoner so he could teach them about humans and humanity.

The androids of this world function to please and serve others. Since its discovery 100 years ago, it has become one of the best known pleasure worlds, second only to Argelius.

RECOMMENDATIONS TO TRAVELERS The androids who run this pleasure world welcome visitors of all races. They have a capacity for learning that is infinite, and a curiosity that is practically sentient. Visitors need not worry that the androids will hold them on Mudd's Planet against their will. Their programming requires only that they learn as much as they can, and there are so many visitors that the androids can barely keep up.

This world offers underground, naturally heated grottos with hot springs, advanced in tri-d entertainment, holo suites, restaurants that cater to any palette, gambling, adult entertainment of every variety, museums and more.

The hotel rooms are first class, with nearly every luxury you could ask for. Rates are reasonable, and Mudd's Planet takes every known Federation currency and credit card. They also take non-Federation currencies.

The leader of the androids is named Norman. He coordinates all functions of the androids from a central complex. The temperature in this world's underground caverns is kept at a constant 72 F.

FACTS TO TAKE INTO ACCOUNT The surface of this world is uninhabitable for humanoid life forms. The history of this world is uneventful. It has never contained native life of its own, and is composed mostly of iron ore, granite, and volcanic rocks left over from the planet's volcanic age when it was newly formed.

There is no atmosphere. The air in the underground chambers is artificially maintained by the androids. Currently, due to the popularity of this world as a vacation spot, the androids are expanding the caves and tunnels to accommodate more visitors. Their hotels are currently booked up for the next two years. They are also building new androids to wait on and serve the whims of the larger number of tourists expected after the expansion is complete.

The new chambers will be finished within the next year. They are already booking for future visitors in these uncompleted resorts, so make your reservations far in advance before visiting Mudd's Planet.

NEURAL

[See FORBIDDEN WORLDS]

NIMBUS III

This desolate world is known as "The Planet of Galactic Peace," although not unique in that designation. It is a vast desert situated equidistant from the capitol worlds of the Romulans, Klingons and the United Federation of Planets.

This world was chosen as a neutral ground on which dignitaries from the three governments could meet for peace talks. Harsh conditions — high winds, hot during the day, freezing cold at night — discourage most people from living on Nimbus III, though there is a small population of both human and non-humanoid beings.

FACTS TO TAKE INTO ACCOUNT Paradise City, the largest on this world, is a primitive style village with a hi-tech bar and small apartment buildings. Poverty plagues the world.

Water is highly valued and can bring a good income if found in sufficient quantity. Unfortunately, the water table is low. Wells must be dug deeper and deeper to tap underground tributaries.

Plant life does not thrive on this world. Food must be imported.

Poverty and desolation attract criminals hoping to avoid the law. Lawlessness is tolerated more than on more civilized worlds because there are not enough law enforcers.

Ambassadors from the three major known galactic governments — Romulan, Klingon and Federation — used to be stationed here. They had little impact on the planet. The historical peace talks were uneventful.

Recently the ambassadorial quarters have housed not ambassadors but wealthy beings who use the world as a stopping off point. Ambassadors from the three governments no longer live here.

The world has no formal government. It is technically under the combined jurisdiction of Romulan, Klingon and Federation governments.

Nimbus III is not recommended as a tourist attraction. There is nothing here of interest.

Paradise City is small and lacks specialized entertainment. This world is currently reported as slowly being abandoned. Though people still live here, off-world immigration is higher than the birthrate. Not recommended for visiting.

NORPIN V

This famous, class M world is the location of a popular retirement colony. The entire planet is a tropical, lush paradise. It is run for those longing for peace and tranquillity away from the stress of everyday life.

This world has the galaxy's largest golf courses. They are set in lush terrain. It has quiet, temperate beaches, huge natural hot springs, entertainment of the most modern sort and housing that is luxurious and affordable.

Tourism is encouraged.

RECOMMENDATIONS FOR TRAVELERS Norpin V lacks poisonous animal and plant life. It is safe for everyone. Temperature remains between 50 F and 100 F year round, with the average at 72 F. Only the poles suffer extreme cold.

There are waterparks in every town, theatres, resorts and hotels, none of which are ever full. You can drop by this world on a whim, without prior reservations.

FACTS TO TAKE INTO ACCOUNT The history of this world is uneventful. There has never been any evidence found of native intelligent life.

This world was discovered over 90 years ago by one of the first exploration starships, the Potemkin. It took only ten years to colonize. During that time, it was transformed into the lovely vacation spot/retirement home it is today.

The planet is completely owned by the Federation. It is located in one of the safest spots in the galaxy, far from neutral zones and near the peaceful Triste and Stash Systems. Law is strictly enforced on this world. The almost non-existent crime rate encourages people to visit or invest for their future on this world.

There are growth moratoriums. At this time, Norpin V's capacity is not even near full. The planet is three times larger than Earth. The world could comfortably support over one hundred times its present population.

This popular tourist planet is on the top ten highly recommended list of the Federation Tourist Bureau.

FOCUS On:

NORPIN V: This world is a popular tourist attraction on the top ten highly recommended list of the Federation Tourist Bureau. This world has the galaxy's largest golf courses amid lush terrain. It has quiet, temperate beaches, huge natural hot springs, a variety of modern entertainment and luxurious, affordable housing. Tourism is encouraged.

Norpin V lacks poisonous animal and plant life. It is safe for everyone. Temperature remains between 50 to 100 degrees Fahrenheit year round; the average is 72 degrees. Only the poles suffer extreme cold.

There are waterparks, theatres, resorts and hotels in every town. None are ever full. You can drop by this world on a whim without reservations.

NOVACHRON

novachron

Not much is known about this mysterious world. Rumor says Novachrons are humanoids. Their highly advanced civilization has peacefully existed for tens of thousands of years.

Their life-spans are incredibly long, and they may be true immortals. No one knows how long they have had space travel. Theorists estimate they have been traveling through the stars for at least five thousand years.

They may have visited Earth in the past. Legends tell of spacecraft descending to Earth in the 20th century and kidnaping humans for medical testing. Legends on Vulcan give similar accounts.

There is no evidence this occurred, but some believe genetic experimentation continues in the galaxy. The secretive advanced beings are seen by some as diabolical. Since little is known of their culture and nature, some fear their motives for remaining hidden.

This world is closed to tourism. Ships are advised to avoid the system.

The first starship landing party to survey this world suffered no casualties, but were told never to return. This starship was the Constellation, commanded by Captain Matthew Decker. Logs report a stunningly beautiful world with spired cities of spun glass. Reports also include eye-witness accounts of a natural stone labyrinth running nearly halfway across the planet's surface. The incredible array of tightly woven valleys and gullies resembles a child's puzzle maze.

This all-natural site would be one of the natural wonders of the galaxy, but Novachron is closed to tourists and survey teams. Should Novachron open to tourism in the future, this planet will be a popular attraction.

Its shrouded history and secretive people will also be an attraction. It is rumored that special representatives of this world secretly move about disguised as humanoids.

Despite unproved fears held by some, the Novachrons are considered a peaceful people. Starfleet may be cooperating with them on top secret projects. Evidence is not available.

OMEGA IV

On this world, two warring factions, the Yangs and the Kohms, bear a striking resemblance to Terran Yankees and Communists. They were descended from an old Earth colony that preserved past ideologies. The oral tradition corrupted and altered them until only a rough approximation remained.

The Yangs were descended from American colonists; the Kohms from a Chinese colony. Something on Omega IV made them long-lived. This has attracted much galactic attention.

The Federation accepted the Omegans as a lost colony of Earth. It provided assistance and education.

FOCUS ON:

OMEGA IV: Colonized by immigrants from Earth, the planet is a paean to Terra's past. Hotels in the planetary capitol city of Reaganville include the Americana, the Washington Arms and the Lincoln Lodge.

A huge 3-D theatre complex has been built in the likeness of the old 20th Century Pentagon building on Earth. It presents vivid recreations of United States history. There is an American Civil War holosuite of a vast open field blending fantasy with reality. The conclusion of the war can be altered, if one wishes.

Replicas of both the Washington Monument and the Statue of Liberty stand in the Americana Parklands, a few miles from the recreation of Mount Rushmore. They are five times original size.

The largest influx of visitors comes from Earth. America is as much legend as reality and its influence has long dominated the affairs of that planet. Now it dominates the affairs of two worlds.

All restaurants serve American cuisine, with an emphasis on 20th Century fast food. Pizza is a favorite and beings from other worlds have developed a taste for it.

With communism dead on Earth, the Kohms formed an alliance with the Yangs. Over the last century the colonists developed a sophisticated culture that holds staunchly to its roots. Now they are one culture based on a super patriotic American ideology.

Red, white and blue provide the color scheme of buildings, cities and vehicles. The flag of Omega IV, the Omega Glory, is very similar to the American flag of 20th Century Earth.

FACTS TO TAKE INTO ACCOUNT Nature is preserved on this world. It is open for enjoyment by visitors from other worlds.

Hotels in the capitol city of Reaganville include the Americana, the Washington Arms and the Lincoln Lodge. A huge theater complex resembles the 20th Century Pentagon. It presents vivid 3-D recreations of United States history.

There is an American Civil War holosuite in which battles can be reenacted, blending fantasy with reality. The conclusion of the war can be altered, if one wishes. Other possible alterations include preventing the assassination of Abraham Lincoln and witnessing a world in which the South won.

Replicas of the Washington Monument and the Statue of Liberty, built five times the original size, stand in the Americana Parklands, a few miles from New Mount Rushmore. Visitors have mostly come from Earth where America is legend. Its influence has long dominated the affairs of that planet. Now it dominates the affairs of two worlds.

⬡ OMICRON CETI III

A Federation colony was established on this world a century ago. Then they learned of the Berthold rays, which bombard this world. The Federation immediately dispatched a survey team, but they did not expect to find the colonists alive.

What they found surprised them. Not only was everyone very much alive, they were in perfect health. A plant native to this world released airborne spores that gave the colonists immunity to the radiation.

The price was high. Those afflicted by the spores experienced perfect peace and euphoria but lacked ambition to work or create. The colony stagnated. Finally the spores were overwhelmed when hosts experienced strong emotions. The colony was relocated to another world to start over.

Omicron Ceti III now houses a small shielded research center. Researchers study the Berthold rays and the strange plant life. They use a hypo-spray to suppress the negative effects of the spores.

Those who partake of the spores are drawn to each other and attain unique, almost telepathic rapport. The chemical composition of the spores is being studied. It is hoped to be of assistance in the treatment of drug resistant forms of depression in humanoid races.

⌖OMICRON THETA IV

This world is located in the Omicron Theta System. It is famous as the planet on which Dr. Noonian Soong created the android Data. The evil android Lore was also created on this world.

The famed cyberneticist's laboratory is still there. It was discovered several years ago by a survey vessel. Data was aboard. Until then he had no memory of the hidden complex.

The Federation colony on this world was destroyed by a mammoth space creature known as the Crystalline Entity. This creature ravaged colonies until it was killed by the mother of a slain colonist from Omicron Theta IV.

She killed it in violation of Starfleet orders. She was stripped of her position and expelled from Starfleet's scientific advisory committee. Sympathetic individuals in the private sector then hired her for her many years of experience and expertise.

Plans are underway to re-establish the colony on this world. It is presently in the final stages of reconstruction.

⌖ORGANIA

Little is known of this world. Its people are powerful and influential.

Organia is a Class M planet that appears primitive and undeveloped. The natives seem human and act passive. Their physical forms are disguises adopted to deal with other humanoids.

Organians are actually non-corporeal beings who long ago evolved beyond the need for a physical body. They possess great powers.

A century ago, they used those powers to halt a brewing galactic war between the Federation and the Klingon Empire. Although they seem omnipotent, they do not wish to interfere in galactic affairs.

The Organians are represented by a Council of Elders. They are soft spoken and, at one point, seemed to stand by when members of their race were executed. No one died, of course, since the physical bodies were only a mask they wore.

FACTS TO TAKE INTO ACCOUNT Today the Organians welcome visitors to their warm, brown world. They greet people in their human guise and talk philosophy.

This world has no large hotels, restaurants or theater cosmoplexes. It offers a simple life of crude buildings and adobe huts where visitors sit and talk with Organians.

Organians do not merely lecture on their philosophy of life and the cosmic balance, but also listen to what visitors relate about their own life experiences. People come to this world when they have lost touch with themselves and their place in life. Here they rediscover that even in a galaxy filled with countless worlds and many forms of being, each person is important and has their place in the scheme of things.

ORGANIA

The Organians predicted the Federation/Klingon alliance 25 years before it came to pass. Some feel they can predict the future. They insist there is no future or past only a now in which all things exist simultaneously.

A link has been drawn between them and "The Prophets," the beings of the Bajoran Wormhole. The Organians have never said this is so. Nor have they denied it. They only respond, "What does it matter?"

Do not travel to this world for a sun tan, thrills on the beach or a romp in a pleasure dome. Save these for Risa and other shore leave worlds.

A voyage to Organia is a pilgrimage. The beings of this world remember their origins and recall linear time. They understand those who travel across the face of countless worlds to reshape the galaxy. They have moved beyond such demands of humanoid dreams and wish to maintain a link with those who have not.

 *PACIFICA*

The surface of the planet Pacifica is almost entirely water. Ground-based cultures, predominantly Terran, easily adapted to this aquatic world.

Pacifica's amazing array of ocean life, none restrained or captured by colonists, is a wonder to behold. At least one of these species is sentient.

This has yet to be proven. Research continues, and can be followed at the Visitor's Bureau of the Pacifica Indigenous Life Research Lab in Aquatic Sector 23-ALZ.

Artificial floating islands allow tourists to beam down to hotels from the space station in geocentric orbit. The Hilton and Holiday Inn chains built islands anchored in the southwestern hemisphere. Few storms plague that location.

Typhoons are commonplace in the far northern hemisphere. That part of the planet has not benefited from colonization.

Pacifica is largely colonized underwater in vast domed cities. The first named itself Atlantis.

Many of the colonists are from Earth. The second undersea kingdom was named Lemuria.

These cities consist of networks of interlinking domes and tunnels surrounded by bright perimeter lights. The cities achieve a bright, sunlit environment on the ocean floor.

A variety of undersea craft are used on Pacifica, including passenger submersibles and even a huge exploratory vessel. The vessel, named the Jules Verne, is capable of remaining submerged for a full year.

FACTS TO TAKE INTO ACCOUNT Humanity's dreams of exploring the unknown have been transplanted to Pacifica. Colonists grow up dreaming of new ways to study the ancient sea bottom and the ruins of ancient civilizations.

Thousands of years ago, a great cataclysm collapsed a continental shelf. It is now being explored on the deep sea bottom of Pacifica.

One ancient site has been opened to tourism. The ruins can be explored by wearing undersea force field body armor. It enables a person to swim and walk around the ocean bottom without cumbersome attire.

Pacifica is a world of tranquil beauty and deep mysteries. Many feel it calling to them from across the galaxy from the first day they see a holo-vid portraying its rich panorama of colonization and ocean going conquests.

PLANET 892-IV

This forbidden world is now open to visitors. A new government sent an envoy with an entreaty to the Federation asking to open negotiations. The Federation obliged. Some feel the United Federation of Planets bears guilt for the contamination of this world a century ago by the Starfleet vessel, the Beagle.

Like the Iotians, the people of this world are imitative. They latch on to ideas. They transformed their culture into a 20th Century version of Earth's Roman Empire.

PLANET 892-IV

This Class M world is very Earth-like. A century ago, the Federation discovered the repressive Praetorian Guard and its leader, the Proconsul, in charge of this planet.

They had atomic missiles capable of firing on approaching craft. The Federation withdrew to see what would develop. It appears that a nascent religious movement took hold a century ago and overthrew the brutal regime. The deadly televised gladiatorial games, such as "Name The Winner," have ended.

FACTS TO TAKE INTO ACCOUNT Today this world is a democracy with touches of a theocracy. The Proconsul and the Praetorian Guard have been repudiated, disbanded and the former leaders imprisoned. They cannot leave the world to spread their mischief elsewhere.

The new government welcomes tourists. They hope to learn more about life in the Federation. They are presently completing negotiations with the Galactic Inn and Howard Johnson's hotel chain to build the first tourist metroplex on the Sea of the Sun, a huge bay on the northeast edge of the main continent of Raseac.

This is a planet with no name. The natives call it by a word in their language that means "The World." It can roughly be transliterated in Federation Standard as Ynos. The world was recently accepted into the Federation after a ten year study determined that its government is stable.

Basic Federation currency is accepted at the major exchange center at the spaceport of Ramadan. Exchange rates are extremely generous, granting the visitor a great deal of buying power per credit.

FOCUS ON:

RAMATIS III: An archeological paradise unlike Earth, where wars devastated Greco-Roman architecture and 20th Century pollution scarred much of the rest. The people of Ramatis III preserve their ancient architecture as part of their cultural heritage.

Tourism funds preservation of many incredible sights, ranging from the Colossus of Rama to the cyclopean Octagon Castle of the Jurtis Mountains. At half a mile across with walls two hundred feet tall, the painted murals and rock carvings are unrivaled by any other world.

Hotels are limited to the port cities of Wrentor and Zurimak. Tour shuttles spend a full day at each major sight. Some tour packages concentrate an entire week at such places as the Octagon Castle. No world is like Ramatis and no tourist is the same after visiting.

◉ *Ramatis III*

Ramatis III is noted for its magnificent stone architecture, rivaling that of Earth. The elite class on this world is bred for special mental powers. This renders them incapable of speech.

They communicate through telepathy. It takes the assistance of three others, who serve as a "chorus," translating their thoughts and feelings into words. Riva, the famed Federation negotiator, was one such individual.

This world is an archeological paradise. Unlike Earth, where wars and pollution devastated much of the great architecture, the people of Ramatis III preserved theirs as part of their cultural heritage.

FACTS TO TAKE INTO ACCOUNT Volumes have been written about the stonework of Ramatis III. Archeology students from many worlds come to study these wonders.

Tourism funds preservation of the many sites, from the Colossus of Rama to the cyclopean Octagon Castle of the Jurtis Mountains.

People come to Ramatis III to see the reality behind the holo-vids. They find themselves swept up in a panoramic history unfolding across the length and breadth of an incredible world.

Hotels are only in the port cities of Wrentor and Zurimak. Shuttle tours leave for a full day at each major site. Some tours spend an entire week at the Octagon Castle. No world is like Ramatis. No tourist leaves this world unchanged.

◉ *Rigel II*

Rigel II is a shore leave world. Hair strategically covers parts of the bodies of female natives. It is brightly colored in shades of pink and yellow.

Women on this world do not wear clothes, only natural, well-groomed multicolored hair. They are very friendly and have made this world legendary among Starfleet personnel.

Visits to Rigel II are usually not recorded in personal logs lest they be discovered by wives and girlfriends.

◉ *Rigel IV*

Rigel IV is a planet rich in boridium, a durable substance used for tools and primitive weapons. Bureaucrats of this world are highly prized by other planets where less serious pursuits are the order of the day.

Shore Leave worlds hire bureaucrats from Rigel IV to keep things running smoothly so their own officials can indulge in less serious pursuits. They say that the people of Rigel IV are born wearing a business suit.

RIGEL VII

[See FORBIDDEN WORLDS]

RIGEL XII

Rigel XII is a desert planet devoid of indigenous life. It is a dry, storm wrought world with nothing of value except rich deposits of dilithium crystals.

Extensively mined over the past century, remaining deposits must be mined by hand to insure that the delicate crystals remain pure and unflawed for use in starship technology. It is a hard life but a man can mine enough crystals to retire in five years.

Not everyone is tough enough to engage in the manual labor. Heavy manual labor is unknown on modern worlds. Few people are willing to do it, in spite of the rewards.

RISA

[by Kay Doty]

Risa was designed as a vacationer's paradise. The visitor finds fine lodging, exquisite dining, theaters, gaming rooms and art galleries.

The lonely visitor in search of companionship finds numerous escort services. Besides very hospitable Risans, entertainers have been imported from throughout the galaxy. The discerning individual can easily obtain the company of his own kind.

A large round stone found on Risa is called the Horga'hn. It is considered a symbol of sexuality, which grants powers to its owner. Openly displaying the stone indicates the wearer is seeking Jamaharohn, a word roughly translating to "sexual contact."

Besides pleasure palaces and games of chance, Risa provides sporting contests to satisfy every taste.

Tours of the mountain regions can be arranged. Underground tours of the many caverns are available during the milder months. Warm clothing and strong walking boots are a necessity for these tours.

Risa has excellent convention facilities, meeting halls and specialized laboratories for hands-on seminars.

STATISTICS One Risan year equals 307.2 Earth days. A day equals 22.7 hours. Temperatures vary from 6 C in mountainous regions to a balmy 50 C to 60 C in temperate zones. Changing seasons bring periods of extreme heat or cold. Climate control is used for the benefit of tourists.

GEOGRAPHY One continent (14,841,707 square miles) holds most of Risa's resident population. All seven large islands and over half of the smaller ones are inhabited. The larger islands range in size from 845,770 to 619,311 square miles. The smaller islands are all 7,372 square miles or less.

An exact census has never been taken due to an inability to count members of the innumerable primitive tribes living on smaller islands. They fade into the landscape when strangers approach.

Islands are not open to visitors. Maps, with the prohibited areas marked in red, are available at the Information Center.

Most entertainment facilities are located in the middle two-thirds of the main continent. Those seeking a more secluded setting will find exquisite accommodations at a higher price on the larger islands.

The mountains are among the most beautiful in the galaxy. They delight climbers, skiers and snow enthusiasts. Seven peaks tower 30,000 feet or more into the stratosphere, while twenty-seven exceed 20,000 feet. Except for the areas that have been cleared for ski runs, dense forests cover the mountain sides.

Heavy foliage hides a network of caves that can extend eight to ten kilometers into the interior. They are a spelunker's dream come true.

Risa is the source of Startithium ore. The substance interferes with sensor readings taken on the planet's surface.

HISTORY Risa was not always a recreation haven. Before the warp drive Risa was an archaic world. The governing body was called the Council of Ten. It settled disputes, made laws and punished those who committed criminal acts.

They appointed teachers and oversaw the development of mines when it was learned the black, hard rock made an excellent fuel. Only the strongest men were allowed to dig for the black rocks.

The bright pieces of colored stones that clung to the valuable fuel source were discarded along with the dirt. Some were used to decorate clothing and homes, or for children's toys.

Woodcutters provided trees builders used for houses, and carvers fashioned into furniture, utensils, decorative items and toys. Sowers planted seeds for food, then left it to go on to a milder climate to start the process again. Others remained behind to harvest the crops.

Hunters provided game for the table and hides for food. Others fished in the great rivers.

Work was hard but the pleasant climate provided relaxation. Team games developed and retain their popularity for both Risans and their visitors. Many Risans believe the tribes on the small islands still live in this fashion.

ADVENT FROM OFF-WORLD The first space ships stopped on Risa during the early days of exploration of the galaxy. Crews were delighted with the planet. They enjoyed the warm weather and soaked in the sunshine after long periods aboard ship.

To the astonishment of the inhabitants, these strangers from the sky were willing to trade their food, clothing and other marvels for carved pieces small enough to carry in their ships. They especially wanted the bright colored stones.

RISA

The Council of Ten soon realized more ships would come to their world if sleeping quarters were available. Then crews could remain on Risa longer, and perhaps make more purchases.

The Council conferred with a ship's captain. He suggested that crews, looking for respite during long voyages, would welcome relaxation on solid ground. When the captain mentioned compensation for such accommodations, the Ten were sold.

They put builders to work constructing small sleeping quarters. The best cooks were engaged to cook food to be sold in eating stalls. Shops soon added a variety of wood items. They sold faster than the carvers could make them. Most popular were the colored stones. This puzzled the Risans, who thought the stones were useless.

When a cargo ship made a second stop, some of the crew wore the stones in beautiful settings. Another business began.

Using natural talent, and excellent advice from the Federation, Risa became one of the most popular resorts in the galaxy. This transformation took place in less than half a century.

As shipping lanes expand, more worlds join the Federation, and warring worlds make peace and venture into outer space, Risa reaps the benefits.

POINTS OF INTEREST Risa's most prominent tourist attractions are the many elaborate entertainment clubs and hotels that line Recreation Boulevard of Capitol City. Smaller towns in outlying areas feature similar, but less lavish, pleasure palaces. This is even true of the big islands.

As Risa's wealth and contact with other species has increased, so has their interest in the universe around them. This curiosity has led to the building of art and historical museums, a library, research center, schools and theaters.

Most are open to the public, including schools. Visitors sit and observe classes, and are encouraged to conduct workshops and seminars for the students, using material from their home worlds.

The theatrical and music commission spent many years collecting play manuscripts and musical scores from around the galaxy. They now possess an excellent repertoire of operas, musicals and stage plays. The three theaters featuring matinee performances are well attended and reservations are not required. Most evening performances play to full houses, and reservations are required.

FACTS TO TAKE INTO ACCOUNT The Risan people are scrupulously honest and expect the same from others. Anyone caught breaking Risa's strict laws against cheating at gambling or theft are required to make restitution to their victims.

The culprit is deported to his ship, and banned from the world for periods of time based on the severity of the crime. If the offender does not have a ship in orbit to return to, h/she is confined to quarters for two days. If at this time no means of leaving the planet has become available, the lawbreaker is put to work at menial tasks in the mines far from the city.

All standard Federation currencies are accepted.

⊚ROMULUS

The home worlds of the Romulans are located in the double star system of Romii. Just as the system has two stars, there are twin worlds called Romulus and Remus. These are basic Terran transliterations of the actual Romulan names for those worlds.

Romulus is the more grand of the two worlds. The few off-worlders who have visited speak highly of the firefalls of Gal'gathong and the Apnex Sea. Another point of beauty is the Valley of Chula where flowers bloom only at night and can be observed opening at sunset through infrared goggles.

Romulans are an offshoot of Vulcan. They broke off before the Vulcans adopted the philosophy of Surak. Romulans remain an aggressive warlike culture.

This split is more than philosophical. Romulans, unlike Vulcans, have no telepathic powers. This technique may have been discovered and taught by Surak.

Romulan and Vulcan law both contain the "Right of Statement" in which the accused has the right to explain the crime they have been accused of. This is one of the few similarities as the Romulans also believe in the "Right of Vengeance," a very un-Vulcan idea.

THE ROMULAN REGIME Romulans remain so aggressive they rarely take prisoners in battle. When captured they choose suicide, including the destruction of their own vessel.

Romulan culture is gender neutral. Women are as likely to command a starship as are men.

Romulans retain a militaristic society. Two hundred years ago, the Romulan idea of manifest destiny collided with the Federation ideal of cooperation and self-determination. War resulted.

The war ended when a neutral zone was created around the Romulan Empire. They could not expand out and no non-Romulan vessel was allowed in. This makes travel to the Romulan Empire very difficult and time consuming wrought with miles of red tape and approvals.

The highest rank in the Romulan Empire is Praetor, their equivalent of king or emperor. He rules all Romulans. Succession to Praetor is from the military.

The Romulan military regime is paranoid. The imperial intelligence force is called the Tal Shiar. A kind of secret police, their power is absolute. They have authority even over the commander of a starship. Their orders are not to be questioned under pain of immediate imprisonment or death.

FACTS TO TAKE INTO ACCOUNT The Federation doesn't prohibit contact with the Romulans. The Romulans do not welcome it and are suspicious of anyone wanting to visit. They suspect non-Romulans of being Federation spies.

Each year, less than one percent of all applicants are granted visas. The closest Federation outpost to the Neutral Zone is Starbase 10. They are closely monitored by Romulan vessels.

ROMULUS

Those granted visas to visit the Romulan Empire contact their official Romulan transport near Starbase 10. An official Romulan "guide" is assigned to every visitor to insure that only non-military sights are viewed.

A Century ago the Romulans had a military alliance with the Klingons. Once the Klingon Empire signed a full peace treaty with the Federation, the Romulans became suspicious of the Klingons. They broke off all contact after the Romulan attack on Khitomer.

The Romulans had already broken off all contact with all other worlds outside the Neutral Zone. After many years, they renewed contact after outposts were mysteriously destroyed on both sides of the Neutral Zone.

It was later determined that the Borg were behind this. The Romulans chose to only observe when the Federation and the Borg clashed at Wolf 359.

Until the Enterprise-D made contact with a Romulan warbird several years ago, there had been no Federation contact for 53 years, the time of the Tomid Incident. The hostile

FOCUS ON:

POTLIGHT ON RISA: Risa was designed as a vacationer's paradise. The world offers fine lodging, exquisite dining, theaters, gaming rooms and art galleries.

There are numerous escort services for the lone visitor in search of companionship. Besides hospitable Risans, entertainers have been imported from throughout the galaxy to meet every taste.

The theatrical and music commission spent many years collecting play manuscripts and musical scores from around the galaxy. They now possess an excellent repertoire of operas, musicals and stage plays. Three theatres feature matinee performances that do not require reservations. Most evening performances play to full houses, and reservations are required.

Risa's most prominent tourist attractions are the many elaborate entertainment clubs and hotels that line Recreation Boulevard of Capitol City. Smaller towns feature similar, but less lavish, facilities. All currencies from both Federation and non-Federation worlds are accepted.

Risa is attempting to draw tourists from the Gamma Quadrant. Rumors indicate this world has courted highly unusual guests.

action left neither side satisfied, although the Romulans now refuse to discuss the incident.

INSIDE THE NEUTRAL ZONE The Federation distrusts the current Romulan regime. The regime was exposed as being involved in the recent power play in the Klingon High Council, and attempting to invade Vulcan. The Romulans have not given up their dreams of empire.

The Norkan Massacre was an attack on a non-aligned world. The Romulans refer to the incident as the Norkan Campaign. The Federation distrusts Romulans as much as Cardassians, although there is more open communication with Cardassia.

Nelvana Three is a world inside the Neutral Zone. It was used by the Romulans to lure a Federation starship into a trap. The Romulans were thwarted by their old allies, the Klingons.

Iconia is also inside the Neutral Zone. It holds the ruins of a 200 thousand years old civilization and artifacts of a technology not yet rediscovered elsewhere. A Federation team explored this world, arousing the Romulans.

Eden is one planet in the Neutral Zone the Romulans thought no one would want. When a group of Federation dropouts fled to that world, most were killed by poisonous plant life.

The world is clearly no Eden. It is believed Romulans once used this world as a chemical dumping ground but they refuse to discuss it. They insist the world is inside the Neutral Zone, and, by treaty, their concern alone.

CLOAKED IN THE PAST The most important device in the Romulan arsenal is their cloaking technology. This allows a vessel to be invisible to sight and sensors. A treaty with the Federation prevents Starfleet from developing similar technology. Why the Romulans do not know the Klingons have this technology, and use their vessels in Federation undercover assignments, remains unexplained.

The latest Romulan experiment with cloaking technology is the Interphase Generator. It enables a person to be invisible and intangible. This technology has not yet been perfected.

The Federation has evidence that one experiment with it was partially successful, if uncontrolled. The presence of a person using Interphase technology can be detected by higher than normal levels of Kroniton particles.

Romulans often claim uninhabited worlds only after something of value is discovered. When a completely unique and ancient life form called "Tin Man" was discovered near Beta Stromgren, the Romulans claimed the world. They attempted to prevent the Federation from communicating with it. "Tin Man" finally made the decision for itself.

Romulans do not accept Federation currencies. Obtaining Romulan barter requires exchanging items they find precious. Otherwise the few visitors allowed must bring food and continually shuttle between Starbase 10 and the twin worlds.

This also insures that visitors will not have much time to elude the watchful eyes of their "guides."

ROUSSEAU V

◈ ROUSSEAU V

This planet was almost destroyed by tectonic activity. Its inhabitants succeeded in preserving their civilization by reuniting the world with neutrino clouds.

Upon close inspection, this world appears to be a collection of asteroids floating together but always maintaining equidistant to avoid collision. Cities and colonies exist on these shards of Rousseau Five. Anti-gravity belts enable inhabitants to "swim" between pieces of their shattered world. Long distance travel requires shuttles.

Many people died in the quakes that cracked Rousseau Five. The survivors are a hearty breed who love their new world and refer to their society as the Rousseau Collective.

It is a unique world with a weak gravity well. People born and raised on this planet are experts at living in a low gravity environment. They find the effects of Earth normal gravity, the standard on Starfleet outposts, crippling. Some work for Starfleet, teaching cadets how to live and work in a low gravity environment.

The scenic wonders of old Rouseau Five are now gone, replaced by new ones. The forest of two hundred foot tall trees was ripped away in the cataclysm.

The Dunryn Crater, site of an asteroid impact a million years ago, miraculously survived. It is odd this relic of an eons old collision still exists while the planet shook itself apart.

The asteroids roughly form the circumference of a circle. This was engineered for aesthetic purposes and to keep a memory of Rousseau Five.

Visiting is not difficult. The space port is within the cluster of asteroids. Visitors find a unique experience in the realities of a shattered world and the use of modern technology to save it.

◈ RUAH IV

This world in the Ruah System is unclaimed by any planetary confederation. It has yet to be mapped and explored.

While the planet is not a forbidden zone it is on the "visit at your own risk" list. It holds unknown dangers. Decontamination after visiting the surface is strongly recommended.

Safety procedures may be unnecessary as Ruah Four appears to be a perfect Class M world. It seems fertile and ripe for colonization. The other planets in this star system are, like Ruah Four, uninhabited. This one holds the best opportunities for colony building as no terraforming is required.

No threatening indigenous plant and animal life have been discovered but such surveys remain sketchy and incomplete. The Federation is interested in hiring a full survey team with a vessel capable of complete deep planet scans to map this world. The discovery of other Class M worlds in recent years has caused the Federation to fall behind schedule.

RUBICAM III

[See FORBIDDEN ZONES]

RUTIA IV

[by Kay Doty]

Rutia recently ended a war with Ansata. A month after this momentous occasion a Tourism Council was formed. Just days later the council made its own announcement:

"After seventy-nine years of pragmatic isolation from the rest of the galaxy, Rutia IV has opened its doors to visitors from other worlds."

STATISTICS This Class M world has an equatorial circumference of 87,396,000 kilometers. It has two continents, the West and the East. Population of West is 2,679,555 and of the East is 11,243,700.

A year on this world is 18 months. There are 7 weeks in a month, and 9 days in a week. Temperatures vary greatly.

When the quakes ended, the continent known as East enjoyed an even temperate climate in areas near water and sweltering heat in the newly formed desert areas. The continent called West pushed north and, except for a small area along the southern coast, was much colder, with a temperature range of -10 C in winter to 54 C in summer.

GEOGRAPHY Centuries ago the two continents were one. Then a colossal earthquake ripped through the huge land mass. A seventy kilometer wide chasm, created by the shifting land, was immediately filled with water from a tidal wave that followed the quake. This unexplainable and unprecedented phenomenon continued for months at varying degrees of severity.

When the ground stopped moving, and the oceans stayed within their basins, a third of the continent had been ripped away. The smaller portion drifted for over three years before coming to a permanent, stable rest 157,000 kilometers from what many called the "Mother World."

Millions died. There was hardly a building left standing on either of the sections. Communication between the two continents was non-existent. The few boats that had previously been used for fishing and pleasure had been dashed to splinters by the raging sea.

The continents began the monumental process of rebuilding, each independent of the other. A primitive form of communication was devised two years later.

The two new societies, the one in the East eventually called Rutia, the one in the West named Ansata, ultimately found themselves in political conflict and went to war. Finally, the Enterprise helped to bring peace to the world.

POINTS OF INTEREST—EAST (Rutia) Nearly everything is new. Most buildings are symmetrical, rectangular lines relieved by great round columns. The exception is the round capitol palace, the tallest building in the city. Sculptors designed images depicting the planet's past on the building's exterior and artists painted great murals on the interior.

The home of the East government rivals the art galleries of many worlds. The Tourism Council recommends that the visitor allow several hours to enjoy these unique works of art.

The cities have many fine restaurants, theaters, shops and visitor centers. The most unusual place on East Rutia to eat is the elaborate "The Fisherman's Shed," a memorial to the men and women who lived and worked in the old sheds that were built to protect them during the desperate years following the earthquake.

The long coast line provides ample space for those who enjoy swimming and seaside activities.

To the north, on top of a mesa, is Desert Park where 163 species of birds, animals and reptiles can be seen in their natural habitats. Many varieties of plant life can be observed as well. Trails are provided and the visitor is forbidden to leave them. To do so will result in heavy fines and jail sentences.

POINTS OF INTEREST—WEST (Ansata) The most popular attraction on West is the Ansata Caverns, the site where the Ansata Freedom Fighters made their last major stand. The most eye-catching feature is a twice-life-size statue of Kyril Finn.

Gift shops feature momentoes of the various periods in the history of both East and West Rutia.

An entrance and exit system has been drilled into the caverns whose enormous series of rooms are among the largest in the galaxy. An underground river flows through one of the rooms, while another features a staggering display of massive stalagmites and stalactites. There is an ample supply of oxygen whose source is as yet unknown. Marking on the walls is strictly forbidden. Violators will be fined, imprisoned or both and ultimately banished from the planet.

The buildings on West are more rustic but as interesting as on her sister continent. The Fish Plaza is an intricate system of tiny rooms. A different kind of seafood is served in each.

The West art work depicts more of the struggle following the earthquake than of an earlier time. Many pieces are for sale.

The second most frequently visited attraction is the Finn Mountains. These peaks are so high that snow never melts at the upper elevations. Ski runs are plentiful for all degrees of skill. Chalets, where visitors may stay as long as they wish, dot the mountain bases as well at various places along the trails.

Guides and medics are available at special huts on the mountainside. However, if a visitor strays into forbidden areas and becomes lost, it will be up to them to find their own way back to civilization. No local citizen will be asked to risk his life to rescue people who cannot obey the rules.

The Federation Tourist Commission gives Rutia IV only a fair rating because while the Federation recognizes the planet's need and desire to protect their still developing ecosystem, their punishment for those who break the rules is unduly harsh. The Prime

Directive prohibits the Federation from interfering with Rutia IV's laws, rules and legal system.

Another reason for the "Fair" rating is the possibility that there are those who may not honor the truce following the end of the conflict. There have been reports of occasional random sniper fire in the outlying regions. Visiting the planet is not forbidden, but is done at one's own risk.

FOCUS ON:

SPOTLIGHT ON RUTIA IV: The cities of the East (continent) have many fine restaurants, theatres, shops and visitor centers. The most unusual restaurant on East Rutia is the elaborate "The Fisherman's Shed" —a memorial to the men and women who lived and worked in the old sheds during the desperate years following the earthquake.

To the north, atop a mesa, is Desert Park. Natural habitats house 163 species of birds, animals and reptiles. Many varieties of plant life can be observed as well. Trails are provided. The visitor is forbidden to leave the trails under penalty of heavy fines and jail sentences. The long coast line offers swimming and seaside activities.

The most popular attraction on West Rutia is the Ansata Caverns, the site where the Ansata Freedom Fighters made their last major stand. The most eye-catching feature is a twice-life-size statue of Kyril Finn.

Gift shops feature momentoes from the history of both East and West Rutia. The buildings on West are more rustic but just as interesting as those on her sister continent. The Fish Plaza is an intricate system of tiny rooms with a different kind of seafood served in each.

The second most frequently visited attraction is the Finn Mountains. These peaks are so high snow never melts at the upper elevations. Ski runs are plentiful for all degrees of skill, from beginner to double black diamond. Chalets, where visitors may stay as long as they wish, dot the mountain bases and various places along the trails.

◉ *SARTHONG V*

This world contains an important archeological site of ruins from a lost proto-Vulcan colony. As soon as it was discovered, the Sarthongians expelled the archeological team and demanded payment for further excavation rights and even larger payments for any artifacts removed.

The Federation is negotiating but thus far the Sarthongians have been adamant. This has led to unfortunate incidents such as when a cloaked ship beamed down a landing party who pilfered key artifacts from the guarded site. The act made the Sarthongians even more intransigent in their opposition to friendly cooperation.

Unlike the people of Ramatis III, who venerate their archeological sites and wish to share their wonders with the rest of the galaxy, Sarthongians want to profit. They are very annoyed that the only ones who share their approach are the Ferengi.

Visiting Sarthong is difficult. Sarthongians often insist tourists post a large bond until they leave and the government is satisfied nothing has been stolen. The tourist industry on this world is dead.

◉ *SCALOS*

Twenty years ago, the Federation was satisfied the Scalosians had died out. They then opened the forbidden world to visitors.

As recently as 150 years ago, an advanced civilization flourished on Scalos. They were a pre-space flight culture advanced in other ways. Volcanic activity spewed substances into the atmosphere that sterilized males and killed children. The race became extinct.

This created a new ability among survivors. They began to move at super speed. Federation scientists believe this hastened their other biological problems.

Because Scalosian women were not rendered infertile, they hatched a scheme to lure a spacecraft to their world with a distress call. They brought the USS Enterprise, under Captain James T. Kirk.

They wanted the crewmen to father new Scalosian children. Unfortunately the substance that allows humans to accelerate to the speed at which Scalosians lived causes them to die when sustaining the slightest injury. The Scalosians were defeated, and, although the Federation offered to help, they were too proud. They preferred to be masters of their own fate rather than recipients of charity.

The Federation declared Scalos a forbidden world. Remaining Scalosians lived out their natural lives.

Recent survey expeditions confirmed that no signs of living Scalosians have been detected. Plans are underway to open Scalos for colonization. It is believed the cities remain in good condition.

FACTS TO TAKE INTO ACCOUNT Scalosian water, once contaminated with a substance that caused a living being to become super swift, has been purged of this toxin.

The atmospheric substance causing sterilization in adult males and the death of children still floats in the air.

Surveys have isolated this substance. A cure has recently been discovered, too late to save the lost race of Scalos.

Scalos at this time is limited to technologists examining the cities. The Federation has announced that Scalos will be opened to normal tourism in five years. At this time colonization will begin to repopulate the cities.

 ## TALOS IV

[See FORBIDDEN ZONES]

 ## TANTALUS V

A century ago this prison colony became notorious for using the Neural Neutralizer. Dr. Tristan Adams was in charge of the Tantalus prison colony. He developed a device to open the human mind to absolute suggestion.

This could have had many beneficial possibilities for the rehabilitation of violent and dangerous offenders. Instead he went too far, trying to turn people into human robots. He didn't stop with the inmates, but turned his device on the prison staff as well.

When a staffer escaped and was found by a Federation ship, they investigated. The starship crew exposed Adams. Adams was accidentally exposed to his own mind altering device for a prolonged period. He died as a result. After restoring the victims to normal, the Neural Neutralizer was destroyed.

Today the Tantalus V prison colony jails prisoners from throughout the Federation. Prisoners are segregated by planet of origin.

The world boasts a network of orbital satellites to prevent escape attempts. The prison is located on a small continent surrounded by hundreds of miles of a chemical sea toxic to most life forms. There has not been an escape in more than 50 years. Only immediate family members are allowed to visit.

 ## TANUGA IV

This is a medium sized Class M world. It is cool most of the year.

Tanuguans are a cold and unforgiving people. Their government proclaims that a suspect is guilty until proven innocent. This places the burden of proof squarely on the defendant.

When a Federation officer was charged with sabotaging the orbiting Tanuga Research Station, this system of justice swung into action. The satellite had exploded moments after he beamed off.

Further investigation proved Dr. Nel Apgar had been accepting Federation grant money to develop a process he intended to sell to the highest bidder. When the Federation officer grew suspicious, the scientist tried to kill him in a transporter accident. It backfired, destroying the space station.

The Tanaguans accepted the evidence but continued to believe their system of government superior to Federation guidelines. Tourists are advised to take any dispute seriously.

Tourism is sparse on Tanuga Four. Tourists feel they are regarded as potential criminals. The people of Tanuga Four resent accusations of paranoia. They claim the Federation spreads unfair stories about them.

Visitors often feel relieved when they leave. They do not recommend the experience to others.

TARSUS IV

The bitter history of this planet haunts it a century later. Tarsus IV was once ruled by the notorious "Kodos The Executioner."

Kodos was governor when famine struck the colony. Relief vessels were not expected for months. Kodos ordered half the colonists executed to prevent mass starvation before the relief ships arrived.

Then, due to a quirk of fate, vessels from a nearby star system provided assistance. Vessels loaded with supplies arrived only days after the executions. Kodos fled Tarsus IV, but his past caught up with him 20 years later.

Tarsus IV is now a self-sustaining Federation world. An entire continent is devoted to farming, insuring the populace is not dependent on imports. The bitter history of Kodos and the early days of the colony is taught in schools, but it is not heavily emphasized.

Tarsus IV has risen above its unfortunate history. It is a beautifully groomed world known for habitats offering natural environments to endangered species. It is referred to as the "Zoo World," a far more benign designation than it once held.

RECOMMENDATIONS FOR TRAVELERS A lush, beautiful planet with clear night skies filled with brilliant stars. The sky is often used as a backdrop for travelogues. Animals both great and small lounge and leap against the sky at sunset.

The continent Romat is a giant game preserve with forests, mountains and a variety of wild kingdoms approximating several Class M worlds. Hotels, including the Discovery and the Hilton Habitat, are located in the two coast cities of Vormel and Natu. Each hotel has a full library on all animals living on the continent.

FOCUS ON:

THETA VIII: Curious travelers have patronized the Hotel Royale since its discovery. They must follow strict procedures set by Starfleet. The Royale operates a repeating program simulating the unknown aliens who constructed it centuries before. Visitors are swept up in the program, assuming roles they must play to leave the hotel.

The Hotel Royale on Theta VIII is more of a conversation piece than a four star experience. The style and decor are strictly early 21st Century. The Hotel Royale has been described as the experience for the person who thinks they've already seen it all and done it all.

TAU CYGNA V

Tours are available, but shuttles do not land. The people of Tarsus IV consider the preserve an almost sacred place that cannot be trammeled by boots and picnics.

Tarsus IV has risen above a dark history to become a bright spot in the Federation.

 TAU CYGNA V

[See FORBIDDEN ZONES]

 TERELLA

[See FORBIDDEN ZONES]

 THASUS

This strange planet seems uninhabited but is the home of an ancient and powerful race. They are a small number of non corporeal beings.

Charlie Evans, orphaned when a ship crashed on Thasus, was raised by these beings. When he was rescued years later, he did not reveal that the Thasians rescued him. After the youth exhibited incredible powers taught him by the Thasians, the truth was revealed.

Charlie killed people by misusing his powers. A Thasian tracked the boy to the starship, but he didn't want to return. His incredible powers made him a threat to normal society.

FOCUS ON:

TARSUS IV: Tarsus IV is a beautifully groomed world known for its vast stretches of animal preserves. Species native to this world, as well as others, are kept in environments approximating the animals' natural habitats. An effort is made to save endangered species. It is sometimes referred to as the "Zoo World."

A lush and beautiful planet, the skies are so clear at night that stars are particularly brilliant. Animals both great and small lounge and leap against the sky, particularly at sunset where the amber sky dips rapidly into darkness due to the speed of the planet's rotation. The sky is often used as the backdrop to travelogues.

Hotels, including the Discovery and the Hilton Habitat, are located in the two coast cities of Vormel and Natu. Each hotel has a full library on all animals living on the continent and tours are available.

Charlie lived out his life on Thasus, finally learning to achieve the disembodied state of his mentors. He still lives there. Much older and wiser in the use of his abilities, Charlie no longer desires contact with physical beings.

Thasus is a medium sized world covered with deserts and mountains. Surveys indicate that eons ago it was rich in plant and animal life. Those days are long gone.

Visitors explore Thasus unmolested. It is rare for a Thasian to contact an explorer. Relics of their ancient civilization are locked deep below the surface in impenetrable caverns even sensor probes cannot locate.

Thasians prefer the company of their own kind. They do not wish to share the remnants of their past with strangers.

THETA VIII

This dark, uninhabitable world in the Theta 116 system is covered with a toxic atmosphere. It also contains a Terran hotel called The Royale!

This hotel was created by long departed aliens who rescued an astronaut from Earth who had become lost in space. Unable to return him to Earth, they did the next best thing. They constructed a remarkably Earth-like hotel populated with robots, all based on a novel which Colonel S. Richey had with him.

All this happened 300 years ago. A few years ago a Federation vessel discovered the hotel with the remains of the long dead astronaut in one room. The aliens constructed the hotel so well it kept functioning long after Colonel Richey died.

Since the discovery of the Hotel Royale, curiosity seekers have become guests of the hotel. They must follow strict Starfleet procedures. The Royale operates on a repeating program based on events in a novel and visitors can be swept into the story. They must play out their new roles to leave without difficulty.

The Hotel Royale is more a conversation piece than a four star experience. The hotel's style and decor is strictly early 21st Century. The Hotel Royale is the perfect experience for the person who has done it all.

TILONUS IV

[See FORBIDDEN ZONES

TRIACUS

This world has a bitter history. A being known as a "Gorgon" was imprisoned on Triacus ages ago by a long dead race.

A century ago, the Starnes Expedition began a colony here, unaware of this deadly creature. When the Gorgon was released, it drove the adults in the colony insane and forced them to commit suicide.

It then adopted a pleasing form and seduced the children into helping. Their affection gave it strength. It could leave Triacus and move on to other worlds to sow the seeds of destruction.

James T. Kirk turned the children against the Gorgon. This destroyed its power.

Triacus has been recolonized. The ruins of the civilization that spawned the Gorgon have been uncovered. The true nature of the creature remains unknown, even a century later. As the Triacus colony grows, the tragedy of a century before fades into memory.

This world is a growing colony not a tourist stopover. In a few years it may draw tourists to explore the ancient history of this world.

⊙ TRISKELION

This warm, green world is located in the three-star system of M24 Alpha. A century ago it was an uncharted planet ruled by three alien entities. They used their powers and knowledge to kidnap members of other races.

The entities forced their captives to fight gladiatorial combat in an arena, entirely for the amusement of the "Providers." The Providers became known as the Gamesters of Triskelion because they bet on the outcome of the battles between their Thralls.

Captain James T. Kirk was one of the captives. He defeated his opponents and demanded an audience with the Providers.

Kirk persuaded them to stop keeping slaves and turn their world into a flourishing colony. He promised this would prove more interesting than betting on which slave kills another. Kirk explained that the complexities of government and society would be more challenging than gladiatorial combat.

The Providers took his advice. They even used the same currency standard, Quatloos, they had used for betting. Thralls were given the choice of returning to their homeworlds or staying to live in the new civilization. Many chose to remain.

FACTS TO TAKE INTO ACCOUNT Triskelions were brought from other worlds. The Providers possessed advanced technology. This was never a struggling, primitive society.

The new Libertarian Collective built an orderly society. They soon requested admission to the Federation.

Every home has a video linkup with the Providers. Their computer-like brains allow hundreds of individuals to go on line at the same time. They engage in conversation, asking questions and obtaining guidance in matters both domestic and scientific.

Triskelion now welcomes visitors. Gambling was outlawed decades ago.

RECOMMENDATIONS FOR TRAVELERS The long-lived Providers continue to provide guidance to their increasingly complex society. These entities never sleep, instead overseeing the safety of the populace around the clock.

Hotels are in the main cities of Shahna and Galt, named after founding members of this growing society. Combats are reenacted for the amusement of tourists.

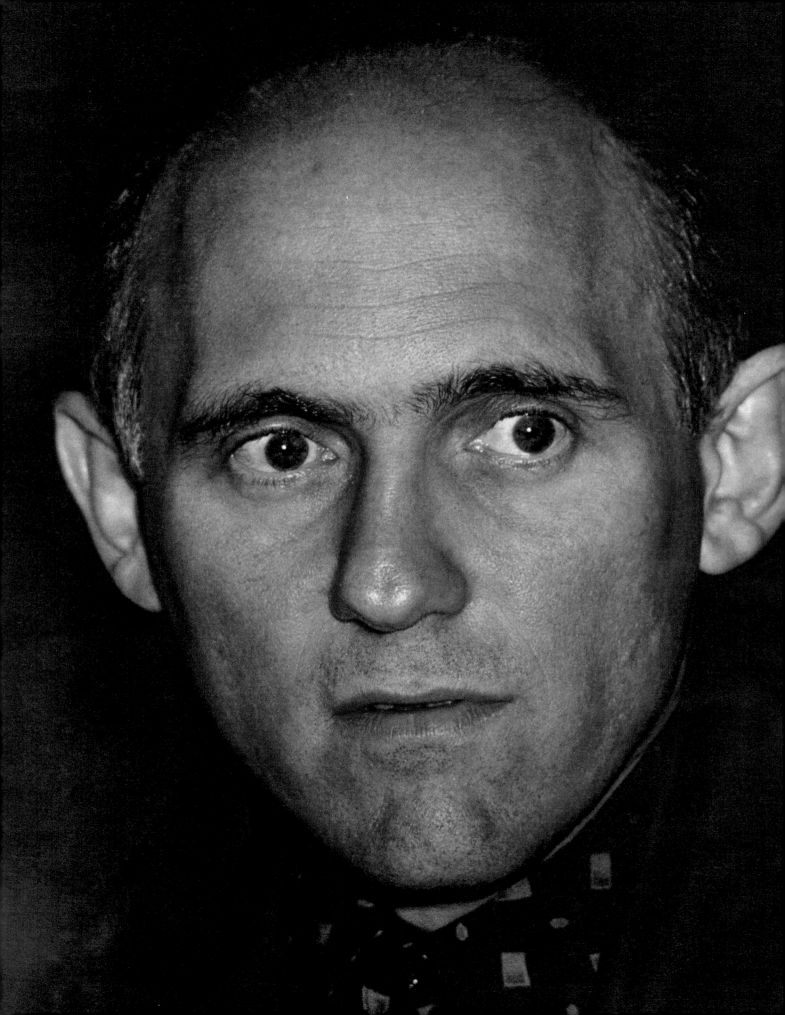

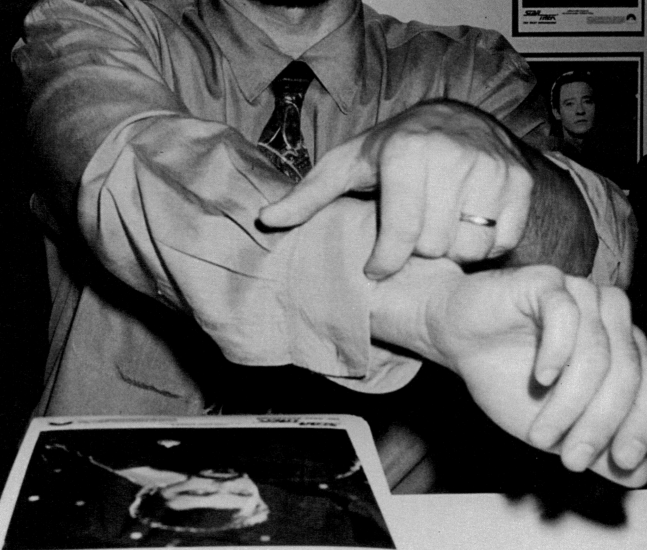

The games have become more like a Triskelion Olympics as athletes vie for trophies. Winners get spacious homes in the mountain top city where the Providers live in their tower retreat.

The Hilton Providor, the Holiday Inn Provider and the Hyatt Regency Provider are the main hotels.

All Federation Standard currencies are accepted.

 **TROYIUS**

[See Elas]

 **TURKANA IV**

[See FORBIDDEN ZONES]

TYRUS VII-A

The mammoth orbiting space station, the Tyan Fountain, is located on this world. It is one of the technological marvels of the Federation.

The orbital mining station employs a particle fountain to excavate the surface of Tyrus VII-A. The Federation closely observes the progress of this device ready to shut it down when it appeared to be malfunctioning and dangerous.

The project director, Dr. Farralon, proved she could succeed with her Exocomps. The mini workdroids enter areas too small for a living worker and repair virtually anything on the Tyan Fountain in record time.

Controversy arose when these small droids developed sophisticated mechanical intelligence including self-realization and self-preservation. Some insist they must be considered a new life form. If so, forcing them to work could be considered enslavement. Dr. Farralon and Commander Data disagree on this.

The Tyan Fountain has received a steady stream of visitors since this debate began. The visitors include robotic experts, cybernetisists and philosophers. The Federation is still examining the robot life and has yet to make a final judgment.

Tyrus VII-A is rich in mineral deposits, some buried deep in the planet. They would have been impossible to mine without the Tyan particle fountain.

The success of this device is closely watched by other worlds with mining problems. The Horta of Janus VI do not take well to journeys of more than a few days. The Tyan Fountain points the way to the future of mining.

RECOMMENDATIONS FOR TRAVELERS The Tyan Fountain is in orbit. Three huge continents embrace two gigantic inland seas on the surface of the large, blue-green world below. Lovely cities welcome tourists to their year round temperate climate. The three continents of Tureng, Burduo and Rendron all feature resort complexes.

Tureng is a winter resort in the far southern hemisphere. The tilt of the axis of the planet creates winter in this region year round. A huge ski chalet waits in a winter wonderland.

Burduo is an equatorial continent similar to Africa in the 18th Century. It is still being mapped and explored.

Ancient cities have been discovered. Two contain remnants of the culture of Tyrus VII-A from centuries ago. This amazing paleontological find offers many perfectly preserved buildings in a culture unspoiled by modern technology. Visitors are carefully controlled so as not to contaminate the culture.

An elaborate year-round summer resort of beaches and lakes with wave machines and hotels with lakeside rooms sits on Rendron. The Embassy Beach Hotel is a beautiful place to visit.

FOCUS ON:

TYRUS VII-A: This large, blue-green world has three huge continents embracing two gigantic inland seas. The most lovely cities in this quadrant of the galaxy can be found on Tyrus VII-A. They welcome tourists to their temperate climate all year round.

The three continents, Tureng, Burduo and Rendron, each feature resort complexes.

Tureng, in the far southern hemisphere, is a year-round winter resort. A huge ski chalet offers a variety of technological methods for exploring the full limits of this icy retreat.

Lying along the equator, Burduo is similar to Africa of Earth in the 18th Century. It is still being mapped and explored. Ancient cities are still discovered. Two contain remnants of the culture of Tyrus VII-A from centuries before, an amazing paleontological find. Many ancient buildings are perfectly preserved, unspoiled by modern technology.

Rendron has a year-round summer resort of beaches and lakes with wave machines and hotels with lakeside rooms. The Embassy Beach Hotel is a beautiful place. Each resort offers restaurants specializing in the culinary delights of the different quadrants of Tyrus VII-A; very different food arose in different parts of the globe. Tourists are invited to "Eat your way across Tyrus," with all Federation forms of currency exchange gratefully accepted.

VAGRA II

[See FORBIDDEN ZONES]

VANDOR IV

[See FORBIDDEN ZONES]

VELARA III

[See FORBIDDEN ZONES]

VENDIKAR

[See EMINIAR VII]

VENTAX II

The advanced civilization of this world has lived in peace for a thousand years. Its rich history is filled with cultural diversity.

The legend of Ardra tells that a thousand years ago the people of Ventax II signed a contract with a demigoddess named Ardra. They would give the world to her in a thousand years in exchange for peace and prosperity for those ten centuries.

After a thousand years of peace and prosperity, in the 24th Century a woman calling herself Ardra appeared in the Council chamber to claim her due. She demonstrated superhuman powers, including the ability to create earthquakes.

She wanted to take whatever she craved of the world. A Federation starship responded to a call for assistance. They proved she was operating from a cloaked ship using modern technology in her charade. "Ardra" was imprisoned for attempting to plunder an entire world!

FACTS TO TAKE INTO ACCOUNT Ventax II is 8,000 miles in diameter. It has three major continents and two smaller subcontinents. Weather control insures that the farming belt gets the rainfall it needs while tourist townships get light rainfall only at night.

The sprawling townships have their own spaceports. Pneumatic transport tubes link the landing facilities to major hotels. One popular resort is named Ardra after the legendary figure in Ventaxan mythology.

The seaport of Ardra has a facility for ocean going vessels of centuries past. The township looks like a five hundred year old city. This creates an illusion of stepping into the past.

The tourist hotel is a domed enclave beneath a nearby hillside. Above ground is a blue, sward covered hill towering over the area a mile from the township. Transport tubes link the underground hostelry with points around the seaport.

Visiting Ardra allows people to experience life in simpler times while enjoying modern conveniences. Some hardy souls choose to camp outside under the stars for part of their stay.

Ventax II is highly rated and not yet overcrowded with tourists. The huge land masses and the many tourist townships insure that this may never happen.

VILMORAN II

This world is a dry, desolate, rocky planet with patches of lichens where life once flourished. This old world is in its declining years, although it enjoyed a fulfilling history.

When the late Prof. Galen discovered a genetic link between all humanoid races, the final piece was found on this world. When the pieces fit together, a hologram revealed how a race of extinct humanoids had seeded the galaxy.

These humanoid life forms adapted to their own worlds in different ways. All of them, Klingons, humans, Romulans, Cardassians and more, share a common heritage. This was the legacy of the final link found on Vilmoran II.

The world became a shrine to the future and a symbol of a unified past. Many travelers visit every year.

VULCAN

The hot, arid planet Vulcan suffers temperatures hotter than most Class-M worlds. Its many deserts of sand blown stone have a spartan grandeur.

Bring eye protection. Direct sunlight caused Vulcans to evolve a nictating second eyelid. Unless your species has this handy backup system, a pair of RayBans is a good investment.

There's not much in the way of fun and games on Vulcan. Most beings who choose to visit are drawn by philosophy not ordinary sightseeing. The landscapes hold profound spiritual significance for Vulcans. A knowledge of Vulcan beliefs enhances any voyage.

The Vulcan Bureau of Visitor Information can provide texts explaining Vulcan philosophy on a basic level. Be warned, Vulcan beliefs and practices are highly complex. Even simple texts require advanced knowledge.

Access to important sites is limited. The plateau of Gol offers a spectacular view but, as the site of the rite of Kohlinahr, it is an isolated restricted area. Mount Selaya is more accessible despite its spiritual importance.

FACTS TO TAKE INTO ACCOUNT Vulcans are known for their lack of humor. This isn't true. Anyone who spends time with one finds that their wit can be deadly, and delivered in a perfect deadpan.

They are tall humanoids with pointed ears and arched eyebrows. Their skin has a faint green undertone due to copper-based blood. A less obvious physical trait is their second eyelid.

Long ago Vulcans were much like their relatives the Romulans. They were an aggressive race that expanded into space and colonized other planets.

When their violence threatened to destroy their culture, Vulcan character changed.

After a lengthy period of chaos and upheaval, serene Vulcan philosophers such as Surak emerged. They led the Vulcans to a new way of life dominated by logic rather than uncontrolled passions.

Vulcan colonies on other worlds either withered or created their own culture, like the Romulans. Vulcans lead in science, excelling in subatomic physics.

They resemble ancient Earth Stoics such as Marcus Aurelius. Their underlying views resemble what pre-contact Terrans termed "humanism."

This cornerstone of Vulcan philosophy is the acronym IDIC, "Infinite Diversity in Infinite Combinations." This demonstrates their respect for the intrinsic spiritual value of all living things.

Vulcans are strict vegetarians. They will drink alcohol on social occasions, and easily control its effects. They otherwise have no interest in mind-altering chemicals, despite false Ferengi claims.

RECOMMENDATIONS FOR TRAVELERS Novice space tourists may be concerned about Vulcan telepathy. This is an unwarranted fear. Direct telepathy is strong only between Vulcans, and usually requires physical contact.

A Vulcan will resort to mind contact only in extreme emergencies. Vulcans, unlike some Betazoids, respect privacy. They do not peek into other people's minds.

FOCUS ON:

VENTAX II: Each sprawling tourist township contains its own spaceport and pneumatic transport tubes linking the landing facility with major hotels. One popular resort is Ardra, named after the legendary figure of Ventaxan mythology.

The Ardra seaport has a facility to recreate ocean going vessels of centuries past. The township looks like a city from five hundred years before. A tourist virtually steps into the past.

Although the hotel is a domed underground enclave, it appears to be a blue, sward covered hill towering over the area about a mile from the township. Transport tubes link the underground hostelry with the seaport. Ardra allows visitors to experience life in simpler times while treating them to modern conveniences.

Ventax II is not overcrowded with tourists partially due to the large size of the planet. Huge land masses and many tourist townships are open for business.

VULCAN

They are excellent observers of humanoid nature and may seem to know what you're thinking, but they will not pry. They will second-guess you with implacable logic. Don't let this bother you; they all mean well.

Museum exhibits in the Vulcan Academy of Sciences, best known for its work in subdimensional physics, show intriguing artifacts from the barbarous past. These include crude but effective killing weapons.

For example, the ahn-woon is a bolo-like device once used to strike and strangle foes in Vulcan mating rituals. Rumor has it that such rituals still take place, but Vulcans are mute on these intensely private matters.

FOCUS ON:

VULCAN: Most beings who visit this world are drawn by an interest in philosophical and spiritual matters. This desert world is excessively warm to those accustomed to more temperate Class M planets.

The impressive landscapes hold profound spiritual significance for Vulcans. A rudimentary knowledge of their significance enhances any voyage. Access to important sites is restricted.

The plateau of Gol offers a spectacular view, but as the location of the rite of Kohlinahr it is an exceptionally isolated and restricted area. Mount Selaya, one of the most amazing sights on the planet, is more accessible even though it is a spiritual hub.

Hotels are rare on Vulcan. The clannish natives only associate with off-worlders when they choose to do so. Vulcans traveling on their own world depend on the hospitality of other Vulcans for personal accommodations.

There is a small hotel in ShiKahr, the birthplace of Ambassador Spock. There is also a small resort secreted in the L-Langon Mountains.

The Vulcan Bureau of Visitor Information provides texts explaining Vulcan philosophy on a basic level. Many find Vulcan beliefs and practice so highly complex that even these "simple" texts require advanced knowledge of galactic philosophies.

Famed as diplomats, Vulcans keep such matters out of sight. If you visit Vulcan, you will be welcomed and treated politely, but it is highly unlikely you will see beyond the surface of things.

Hotels are rare on Vulcan. They are a clannish people who only associate with off-worlders when they choose to do so.

Vulcans travel on their own world but depend on the hospitality of other Vulcans for personal accommodations. There is a small, modest hotel in ShiKahr, much visited in recent years because it is the birthplace of Ambassador Spock.

There is a small resort in the L-Langon Mountains.

Remember Vulcan is a desert world and consume sufficient liquids so as not to suffer dehydration. Do not wander off alone as the poisonous le-matya, a huge lion-like creature, is not extinct.

If you need salt on your food, bring a supply. It does not occur naturally on Vulcan.

WORMHOLE

WORMHOLE

[See BAJORAN WORMHOLE]

 **YARROW**

[by Kay Doty]

Yarrow is the fourth and only inhabitable world in the Lictionia solar system. The Lictionia System is located in the least explored corner of the galaxy, just inside Federation territory. Their first contact with another world was on Stardate 6927.1.

Yarrow was briefly occupied by the Kreel. They brutally enslaved Yarrowians as mine workers. Eventually the Yarrowians drove off their captors and entered a mutual protection pact with Starfleet. They chose not to join the Federation.

This tale of the famous rebellion is related to dispel myths and put to rest doubts about whether visiting Yarrow is safe. Yarrowians have renamed their capitol Freedom City and are far more suspicious of visitors than they once were.

FOCUS ON:

YONADA: Yonada recently opened to visitors as it tries to discover its place in the universe. It has only just begun to learn of the wonders of the Federation and Alpha Quadrant.

Yonadans underestimated general curiosity about the generation ship they traveled in. Tourists flocked to Yonada to tour the ship, an achievement of a race from a dead world whose descendants piloted the vessel into orbit around the new world.

Yonadans are overwhelmed by the attention from off-worlders. They have accepted offers from a crazy quilt of hotel operators. There are inns run by Tellarites, Orions, Ferengi and even a Klingon restaurant that features bloody, pitched battles as part of the floor show.

The Klingon Restaurant, A Fistful of Gakh, has proven popular. Other restaurants try to imitate it with their own violent floor shows (with some unfortunate casualties as a result). The Klingons have offered to take on the lunch time warriors at other restaurants but thus far there have been no takers. As one put it, "They fight for real! I'm just an actor!" Klingons are the ultimate method actors, and Yonada has one of the ultimate Klingon restaurants.

 **YONADA**

This is a unique world in the Federation. Its colonists crossed much of the galaxy to reach this planet.

Originally Yonada was not a world but a Generation Ship containing the descendants of the survivors of the Fabrina system. The star Fabrina went nova hundreds of years ago.

Before it did, the Fabrini built an atomic powered vessel disguised as an asteroid. Voyagers were selected from those with valuable skills to hand down to their descendants.

A century ago the planet Daran V detected an approaching asteroid. When a Starfleet vessel investigated, they discovered that the asteroid was a deep space vessel that had gone off course. A course correction put it back on direction.

When the Yonada was discovered, the people no longer knew they were inside a spaceship. They believed their vessel was all there was. The people learned the truth and their malfunctioning Oracle was reprogrammed for when the vessel reached the designated star system.

FACTS TO TAKE INTO ACCOUNT All knowledge of the Fabrini is stored in their Intelligence Files made available when they reached their new world. The Federation improved the technology on the vessel so it would reach the new world sooner.

They christened this world, Yonada. The asteroid ship now encircles the new world as a moon. It is a monument to their ancestors whose efforts and foresight gave them the chance to rebuild their civilization.

Yonada has learned to welcome visitors as it discovers its place in the universe. It is learning of the wonders and perils the Federation and the Alpha Quadrant hold.

The Yonadans (as they now call themselves, rather than Fabrini) underestimated the curiosity associated with their generation ship. Tourists flock to this world to tour the generation ship.

It is an achievement of a race from a dead world. The network of chambers, living quarters and the control center of the ship offer a rare opportunity to view the handiwork of an alien culture.

The Yonadans are overwhelmed by the attention and have accepted a crazy quilt of hotel operators. There are inns run by Tellarites, Orions, Ferengi and even a Klingon restaurant that features bloody, pitched battles as part of the floor show.

The Klingon Restaurant, called The Squirming Gakh, has proven so popular other restaurants attempt to imitate it with their own violent floor shows. The Klingons have offered to take on the lunch time warriors of other restaurants, but thus far there have been no takers.

As one put it, "They fight for real! I'm just an actor!" Klingons are the ultimate method actors.

Yonada has developed a unique cultural flavor amalgamating the best and most unusual of many worlds.

 *ZALKON*

[See FORBIDDEN ZONES]

 ZEON

[See EKOS]

 *ZIBALIA*

This planet is infamous as the home world of Kivas Fajo, the insane collector. He was willing to kill to acquire the rarest items in the galaxy. Fajo was imprisoned after kidnapping Commander Data, the only android in Starfleet.

Zibalia is overpopulated. It is forced to import many of its basic needs. It has developed important technologies to exchange for these goods.

This wealthy world has begun importing not just representations of off-world cultures, but more questionable items, associating with the Ferengi and others. The average Zibalian is fascinated by off-world culture, particularly from Federation worlds. They are captivated by the entertainment products of Earth, and its imitators.

Zibalia developed a movie development company specializing in dramatizations of the medieval period of their planet's history. Then warriors used primitive weapons, rode six-legged steeds and fought in hand to hand combat. Some long for those days.

They set aside undeveloped preserves to reenact past battles. Some involve hundreds of participants. These have been filmed and play to acclaim on other worlds. One of them, "The Shadow Warriors," won the coveted Spielberg Award.

FACTS TO TAKE INTO ACCOUNT This is a world of mild winters. Oceans cover three fifths of the planet. Floating cities and underwater habitats house an increasing population.

Most people prefer to remain on Zibalia rather than emigrate to other worlds. One large group of Historical Resurrectionists moved to a small, newly approved Class M planet. Its climate and topography closely resemble Zibalia of a thousand years ago, although it is only about a third the size of the home world.

They named this new world Akira. It was perfect for recreating cities, castles and an entire nation based on records telling of life on Zibalia hundreds of years before.

The people appear to live as primitively as their ancestors. In reality, they have modern underground colonies. On the surface they dress in period costumes and use only artifacts common in their history.

Life goes on normally on the home planet. The crimes of Kivas Fajo have become an object lesson of what can go wrong when one becomes too self-absorbed in selfish interests.

Zibalia is open to tourists. It strives to be the friendliest world in the Federation to expunge the memory of Kivas Fajo. Zibalians attempt to portray him as uncharacteristic of their world.

TREK: THE MAKING OF THE MOVIES
James Van Hise

TREK: THE MAKING OF THE MOVIES tells the complete story both on-screen and behind the scenes of the biggest STAR TREK adventures of all. Plus the story of the STAR TREK II that never happened and the aborted STAR TREK VI: STARFLEET ACADEMY.

$14.95.....160 Pages
ISBN # 1-55698-313-1

TREK: THE LOST YEARS
Edward Gross

The tumultouos, behind-the-scenes saga of this modern day myth between the cancellation of the original series in 1969 and the announcement of the first movie ten years later. In addition, the text explores the scripts and treatments written throughout the 1970's, including every proposed theatrical feature and an episode guide for STAR TREK II, with comments from the writers whose efforts would ultimately never reach the screen.

This volume came together after years of research, wherein the author interviewed a wide variety of people involved with every aborted attempt at revival, from story editors to production designers to David Gautreaux, the actor signed to replace Leonard Nimoy; and had access to exclusive resource material, including memos and correspondences, as well as teleplays and script outlines.

$12.95.....132 Pages
ISBN # 1-55698-220-8

THE HISTORY OF TREK

James Van Hise

The complete story of Star Trek from Original conception to its effects on millions of Lives across the world. This book celebrates the 25th anniversary of the first "Star Trek" television episode and traces the history of the show that has become an enduring legend—even the non-Trekkies can quote specific lines and characters from the original television series. The History of Trek chronicles "Star Trek" from its start in 1966 to its cancellation in 1969; discusses the lean years when "Star Trek" wasn't shown on television but legions of die hard fans kept interest in it still alive; covers the sequence of five successful movies (and includes the upcoming sixth one); and reviews "The Next Generation" television series, now entering its sixth season. Complete with Photographs, The History of Trek reveals the origins of the first series in interviews with the original cast and creative staff. It also takes readers behind the scenes of all six Star Trek movies, offers a wealth of Star Trek Trivia, and speculates on what the future may hold.

$14.95.....160 Pages
ISBN # 1-55698-309-3

THE MAN BETWEEN THE EARS:
STAR TREKS LEONARD NIMOY

James Van Hise

Based on his numerous interviews with Leonard Nimoy, Van Hise tells the story of the man as well as the entertainer.

This book chronicles the many talents of Leonard Nimoy from the beginning of his career in Boston to his latest starring work in the movie, Never Forget. His 25-year association with Star Trek is the centerpiece, but his work outside the Starship Enterprise is also covered, from such early efforts as Zombies of the Stratosphere to his latest directorial and acting work, and his stage debut in Vermont.

$14.95.....160 Pages
ISBN # 1-55698-304-2

COUCH POTATO INC.   5715 N. Balsam Rd   Las Vegas, NV 89130   (702)658-2090

Use Your Credit Card 24 HRS — Order toll Free From: **(800)444-2524** Ext 67

THE MAN WHO CREATED STAR TREK: GENE RODDENBERRY
James Van Hise

The complete life story of the man who created STAR TREK, reveals the man and his work.

$14.95 in stores ONLY $12.95 to Couch Potato Catalog Customers
160 Pages
ISBN # 1-55698-318-2

TWENTY-FIFTH ANNIVERSARY TREK TRIBUTE
James Van Hise

Taking a close up look at the amazing Star Trek stroy, this book traces the history of the show that has become an enduring legend. James Van Hise chronicles the series from 1966 to its cancellation in 1969, through the years when only the fans kept it alive, and on to its unprecedented revival. He offers a look at its latter-day blossoming into an animated series, a sequence of five movies (with a sixth in preparation) that has grossed over $700 million, and the offshoot "The Next Generation" TV series.

The author gives readers a tour of the memorials at the Smithsonian and the Movieland Wax Museums, lets them witness Leonard Nimoy get his star on the Hollywood Walk Of Fame in 1985, and takes them behind the scenes of the motion-picture series and TV's "The Next Generation." The concluding section examines the future of Star Trek beyond its 25th Anniversary.

$14.95.....196 Pages
ISBN # 1-55698-290-9

COUCH POTATO INC.   5715 N. Balsam Rd   Las Vegas, NV 89130   (702)658-2090

Use Your Credit Card 24 HRS — Order toll Free From: **(800)444-2524** Ext 67